HUMAN RACES

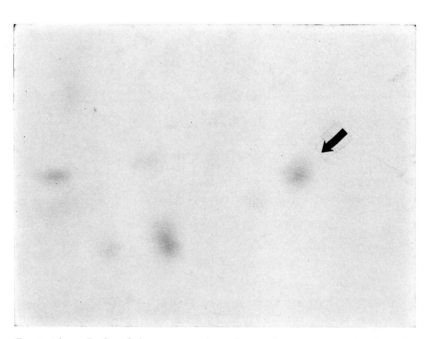

Frontispiece. Reduced-size paper-strip urinary chromatogram showing the presence of various amino acids in the urine (fuzzy-gray spots). In this example, the black arrow points to the area occupied by beta aminoisobutyric acid (β-AIB), an amino acid frequently excreted in quantity by individuals of Asiatic origin. The β-AIB polymorphism shown in this photograph is but one of many differences in metabolism, biochemical functioning and immunochemical properties.

HUMAN RACES

(Third Edition)

By

STANLEY M. GARN, Ph.D.

*Fellow of the Center for Human Growth
and Development
and Professor of Health Development
School of Public Health
University of Michigan
Ann Arbor, Michigan*

CHARLES C THOMAS · PUBLISHER

Springfield · Illinois · U.S.A.

Published and Distributed Throughout the World by
CHARLES C THOMAS • PUBLISHER
BANNERSTONE HOUSE
301-327 East Lawrence Avenue, Springfield, Illinois, U.S.A.
NATCHEZ PLANTATION HOUSE
735 North Atlantic Boulevard, Fort Lauderdale, Florida, U.S.A.

© *1961, 1965, and 1971 by* CHARLES C THOMAS • PUBLISHER
Library of Congress Catalog Card Number: 77-128644

First Edition, First Printing, 1961
First Edition, Revised Second Printing, 1962
Second Edition, 1965
Second Edition, Second Printing, 1968
Second Edition, Third Printing, 1969
Third Edition, 1971

Printed in the United States of America
N-1

2/8259

PREFACE TO THE THIRD EDITION

T HIS IS the third edition of a slim book about race in man. It is concerned with the taxonomic unit below the species *sapiens,* with the higher and lower natural groupings variously termed "stocks," "breeds," "ethnic groups," and "populations" by others, often interchangeably.

This is a book about the natural forces that bring about race, by enforcing reproductive isolation, by bringing about the effects of disease, altitude, temperature, the availability of food, and the lack of food. It is a book about man-made races in man, the products of admixture, and about accidents in raciation—due to small samples, the "founder effect," and the "grandfather effect."

This is a book about genetic change, within races, and ongoing evolution in contemporary man. We are all changing, generation after generation, but at different rates and (often) in different directions. This book is itself changing, through two previous editions and a total of five printings, altered in each printing to bring in new information and to delete some of the old.

What we know of *Kuru* has changed for example. What we think of lactase deficiency is new. We now know more about β-AIB, PKU, the abnormal hemoglobins, and the two forms of G6PDD. We know more about New Guinea and some parts of Africa, and our understanding of taxonomic relationships in South America and Africa has gained in extent, too.

It is not simply out-with-the-old, on-with-the-new. What we learn about living races applies to fossil taxa, as we the living become living models for those now dead and extinct. Is a fossil truly different? Was tooth development in *H. erectus* really different? Study modern men and find out.

Now this book has nothing to do with racism, which is simply the attempt to deny some people deserved opportunities simply because of their origins, or to accord other people undeserved op-

v

portunities only because of their origins. The history of our species is far too long (and periods of national glory far too short) to direct attention away from race as an evolutionary phenomenon to futile arguments about superiority, inferiority, or moral supremacy, which become two-edged and detrimental to all who wield them.

This book is one of a pair. It has a companion *(Readings on Race,* 1960, 1969) which selects original scientific contributions from the broad literature of human biology, human physiology, human ecology, and human genetics. So selected, *Human Races* can be what it is, changing, slightly expanding, and rewritten from printing to printing.

STANLEY M. GARN

ACKNOWLEDGMENTS TO THE THIRD EDITION

As this book is repeatedly revised, it is important to the author but probably boring to the reader to remember those who have helped at the time of its inception and in the steps in its changes. But this third edition includes otherwise unpublished quotations from Dr. Robert Blizzard, Jr. on the endocrinology of Pygmies, Dr. D. Carleton Gajdusek on the transmission of Kuru, and Dr. Roberto Frisancho on race at high altitude. Suggestions made by Dr. Juan Comas and M. Layrisse have been incorporated into the sections on Amerindian taxonomy as have been comments on the taxonomy of Africa and the taxonomy of Melanesia.

Reviews in the professional literature have also brought about changes, from the revised second edition of the first printing on, and including the French Language Edition, published by Vigot Frères and translated by Martial Villemin. If a professional anthropologist mistakes a chromatogram for a photomicrograph (as one did) or misquotes the summary statement on blood groups on race, then the original version was not clear and has been revised. Readers' questions, too, have stimulated textual revisions, for the same reasons.

From the first printing of the first edition on, the publishers have accepted the need to change paragraphs, alter captions, add to tables, extend and amend the suggested readings, and the chapter listings as a whole.

Shirley M. Garrett has had the responsibility for collating the alterations in the last printing of the second edition and for this third edition.

S.M.G.

CONTENTS

LIST OF ILLUSTRATIONS

HUMAN RACES

1

THE NATURE OF RACE

N EARLY two hundred years ago, Carolus von Linnaeus, the great naturalist and taxonomist, set up his famous classification of living things. When he came to man, Linnaeus properly assigned man to the order *Primates* on the basis of numerous and fundamental biological similarities. To the genus that contained man, he gave the traditional Latin name *Homo.* And, having weighed the evidence for and against several species of man, von Linnaeus assigned all living forms of mankind to one species within the genus *Homo,* as *Homo sapiens.*

Today, we know far more about man than Linnaeus did. We have received from the Pleistocene deposits of Java and China fossil species of *Homo* that are quite distinct from *Homo sapiens.* We have come to study many groups of living men quite unknown in Linnaeus' time. Beyond the simple descriptions available to the Swedish taxonomist, we have precise anthropometric measurements, data on blood groups, the haptoglobins, and many measures of biochemical functioning. Although there are some traits in which different human groupings show little overlapping, living mankind clearly constitutes a single polytypic species. Fossil non-sapiens hominids no longer exist, and we are all *Homo sapiens,* as assigned by Linnaeus.

But, within this single species which now covers the habitable globe there are many discrete groupings, some so clear-cut as to be obvious to the least-trained observer, and others less easily distinguishable except after intensive study. These groupings, differing greatly in size and taxonomic status, have commonly been lumped under the single term *race.* Thus, so-called races are grossly distinct by all of the tests we now have and use, while other groups called races differ in smaller degree, in the averages of certain measurements, in the proportions of discrete traits, and in the frequencies of such biochemical differences as the several blood groups.

3

In addition to races defined by zoologists, anthropologists, and human geneticists, human groupings of various kinds have been dignified or designated by the term race. Race has been equated with language, and that is the sole useful meaning of the "Aryan race." Race has been identified with religion, as in the case of the "Jewish race," which in reality comprises a number of discrete populations, some quite unrelated to the others. National groupings have frequently been called races, especially in periods of intensive nationalism. While at times linguistic groupings and biological races may coincide and while religions or even national boundaries may delimit race-populations of various sizes, language, religion and national affinity are hardly measures of race. Race is a biological concept and races are biological units. Races, moreover, are natural units and not artificial assemblages created by selecting "types" out of a population.

A century ago many scholars believed that all human groups could be explained in terms of a few "original" races, usually numbering three. Many attempts were made to explain known human populations as mixtures, in varying degree, of these hypothetical original races. In the days when all dark-skinned peoples were accepted as "Negroes," when all straight-haired people were accepted as members of the "yellow" race, an original set of but three races satisfied the data and fitted the assumptions. Yet, it is now obvious that such a working hypothesis is untenable. No possible combination of Negro, Mongoloid, and White could produce the Australian aborigine. No such combination could explain the American Indian. The blood group distributions in Melanesia, Micronesia, and Polynesia could hardly be explained in terms of Negro-Mongoloid-White admixture. In fact, there is little reason to believe in a system of but three original races, that but three original races ever existed.

In Europe too, scholars formerly postulated the one-time existence of a limited number of "pure" races, which through admixture, gave rise to the complex situation we see from Finland to North Africa today. As proof of their hypothesis, they pointed to the occurrence of *individuals* exemplifying the characteristics attributed to the hypothetical pure races. From blue-eyed, long-headed, light-haired men and women they inferred the "Nordic" race, and from various combinations of features found in individuals, other ancestral "pure" races were similarly deduced.

Yet, while the individuals themselves, as "types," clearly exist, the inference that they recapitulate ancestral strains can be challenged. As Edward E. Hunt, Jr. (1959) has demonstrated, the individual "types" are merely chance combinations of the genetically independent traits. Since the traits are independent and "segregate" out separately, such types as may be found in a population prove nothing about the appearance of ancestral groups. Blue eyes and blond hair are no more proof for an original Nordic race than red hair and freckles point to an original Rufous race, or short stature and heavy beards to a race of Trolls.

In its heyday, however, the approach to race as a series of types led to racial typing of *individuals,* with rather remarkable results. Various members of a single family were often assigned to different "races," and three brothers or three sisters could be typed as belonging to as many different "races" (Fig. 1).

THE CONTEMPORARY APPROACH TO RACE

The contemporary approach to race in man, as in other living forms, is eminently simple. It is a return to the basic principles of classification, to the days before hypothetical original races were postulated and populations were analyzed in terms of varying proportions of different racial "types." Yet the contemporary approach to race stems from population genetics, where a race is viewed as a breeding population, neither more nor less. A race in man, as in any living form, is a *population,* a population of men, women and children, of fathers, mothers and grandparents (Fig. 2). Members of such a breeding population share a common history and a common locale. They have been exposed to common dangers, and they are the product of a common environment. For these reasons, and especially with advancing time, members of a race have a common genetic heritage.

Such a definition, race as identical with the breeding population, transcends history. One race, or one breeding population, may go back 20,000 years, or even more. The Central Australians,

Fig. 1. The concept of race as type. In this approach, where individuals are classified as to appearances, brothers may be assigned to different "races."

and possibly the Andamanese, can claim such antiquity, with little or no admixture. Another race, as for example the American Colored, may have been formed by admixture in recent memory, but it has equal claim to racial status. A third race, far smaller than either of the two mentioned, but no more recent than the American Colored, is the genetically and geographically isolated population of Pitcairn Island. If there is hesitation at calling the Pitcairners a race, how large must a population be to be a race? If admixture, both known and recent, provides a stumbling block to acceptance, how about the probable incorporation of Neanderthals into the European population and the certain addition of late-Paleolithic survivors as late as 8,000 years ago?

From the standpoint of taxonomy, that is, classification, how a race was formed is irrelevant. A race is a race is a race whether it goes back unchanged for six millennia or whether it resulted from admixture after 1850. Our preoccupation with recent history may make us view the neo-Hawaiian race with hesitation, but how about races whose mixed origins barely antedate the written

Fig. 2. The concept of race as population. In this approach, emphasis is on the biological race or population *isolate*.

record? In similar fashion, there is no number test for race. The Bushmen of South Africa, totalling perhaps 25,000, are quite as real a breeding population as the American Colored, who number some 15 million.

Moreover, there is increasing evidence that races do change in their genetic makeup, even in the absence of admixture. The sickle-cell gene, for example, has been on the increase in Africa ever since slash-and-burn agriculture was introduced. With drainage, mosquito control, DDT, and antimalarial drugs, the sickle-cell gene will decrease in generations to come. Differences between races once thought to go back to remotest antiquity, now appear to be genetic responses to environmental conditions. Recognizing that changes do occur within races, that races are not fixed in their genetic makeup, our attention has shifted from the simple existence of races, and the description of the differences, to the mechanisms that bring these changes about.

OTHER NAMES FOR RACE

So far in this book the term *race* has been used to designate natural human populations, the sum of which constitute the species as a whole. To be technical, the "race" is the taxonomic (that is, classificatory) unit immediately below the species. So it is that the single species *Homo sapiens* comprises an indefinite number of races of varying degrees of differentiation and of differing magnitudes, as will be discussed in the next chapter. This is what race means here and as used by physical anthropologists, geneticists, and human biologists.

Because the term race has had some other meaning in the past, as reference to historical literature will show (cf. Count, 1950 and Gossett, 1963), and has been sadly misused by politicians and demagogues, by the Madison Grants, Lothrop Stoddards, and Carleton Putnams, some workers do shy away from the term, preferring substitutes or word-replacements. Some "races" were purely hypothetical constructs, as Sherwood L. Washburn (1944) has pointed out, names for hypothetical populations that never existed. Some "races" were invented purely for political purposes, in the never-never land between fiction and falsehood.

Euphemisms for race include "breed" and "stock" and "strain." The geneticist Hans Kalmus (1950) preferred the latter, and the term "strain" is much used for defined strains of laboratory animals, such as the Wistar rat and the Hooded rat. The word "variety" has been applied to human races as a word with minimal semantic overtones. However strains (relatively homozygous inbred lines, maintained in the laboratory) do not reasonably apply to natural human populations, and the term "variety" *(var.)* has quite different connotations in botany. The terms "stock" and "division," though used in the past, also have particular connotations not quite applicable today.

M. F. Ashley Montagu has urged the term *ethnic group* as a lexical substitute for race, often as a direct replacement, especially for non-scientists (1950), and as a direct equivalent in his more recent writings (cf. Ashley Montagu, 1964). His "ethnic groups" correspond to earlier listings of races. The term "population" is much used today, as a more neutral term with minimal taxonomic implications, and some workers not incorrectly simply name the group under study (Amish, Basques, Dinka, Lacandone, Romans, Parisians, Peruvian highlanders, etc.).

These substitutes have their place in human studies. The Amish are a religious isolate of Western European origin and are included in the European geographical race. The Basque are of Franco-Spanish locale, differing in some ways but not in others from Southern Europeans. Amish and Basque constitute natural groupings of different origins and different degrees of historical differentiation. They are of different taxonomic levels.

To be sure it is not of burning importance which term is used if it is well and properly defined. A rose, says Shakespeare, is a rose is a rose. A race is a race is a race whether it is called *race,* or *race-population,* or ethnic group or ECAR, which is simply race spelled backwards. Natural populations of man clearly exist below the species level. They need labels, and the labels must distinguish between the large geographical or continental collections and individual population isolates. Eskimos and Amish are not taxonomically identical human units.

A newly minted, specially coined word might be employed by common agreement, to refer to groupings below the species level. We may yet agree on ECAR. Like *atom* (which originally meant the unsplittable), the concept of race has changed with increasing knowledge. For the moment we will continue to use the term race for the unit below the species, noting some operational similarity with "ethnic group" when the latter is correctly used, and that all races are *populations* (of various kinds of complexity), but that all populations are not races, in turn.

ETHNIC GROUPS AND NON-RACES RACES

Non-biological uses of the term *race* by politicians and others, as well as obvious popular misuses (for example, the "human race") have occasioned word substitutes, as described above. One such is "ethnic group," properly a culturally defined group, hardly an exact semantic equivalent replacement. As Ashley Montagu put it in the Cold Spring Harbor Symposium of 1950, "I am merely suggesting that, where there is no doubt, we continue to use the term race, but that where there is any doubt whatever we, as scientists, use the phrase ethnic group." Still, in the index of his book *The Science of Man* (1964) race is listed simply as "see ethnic group," and the table of "ethnic groups" given closely resembles listings of races as used in the 1930's.

Writing in a compendium published in 1964 (and arranged by Ashley Montagu), C. Loring Brace proposed "a non-racial approach towards the understanding of human diversity." There he mentions, among others, Australian aborigines, Congo Pygmies, Hottentots, Southeast Asiatics, New Guinea natives, North Chinese, Polynesians, etc. As with ethnic groups that correspond 0.7 with listings of races, "non-races" and races (see Chs. XII and XIII) obviously have very much in common.

There are, after all, many natural human populations that are well defined and well known. The Bushmen are one such, whether they are viewed as a local race or a higher taxonomic unit, a non-race race or an ethnic group. Eskimos are another such example, though differences between Greenland Eskimos and Alaskan Eskimos and Aleut pose problems both taxonomic and phylogenetic. Northern Europeans differ from Southern Europeans, biologically as well as in terms of culture history. Jews are ethnic groups in the correct sense, yet most groups of "Jews" preserve some indications of their Mediterranean origin, even though the Jews from Vilna and those from the Yemen are now poles apart in the rarer enzymatic and disease polymorphisms.

It is a relatively simple task to define gene frequencies in the Navajo. It is less easy to describe just how different the Navajo are from the Apache and how both groups fit (out of original Canadian context) among the American Indians of the Southwest. These taxonomic and phylogenetic problems are not solved simply by calling them populations, or ethnic groups, or races, or non-races.

LIVING MAN AND FOSSIL RACES

The study of fossil man is to the largest extent inference as to extinct races, that is, taxonomic units below the species level in now-ancient man. Students of human paleontology would prefer it otherwise, for taxonomy below the species level from bones alone is a tacky task. But all hominids are *Homo,* there goes the genus, most are *sapiens,* and we have passed the species! What is left is clearly fossil races.

Being subgroups of *H. sapiens,* Neanderthals are—at best— races. Of the *erectus* hominids, those of China, Java, and Africa may be not more than races. If Australopithecus and Paranthropus are both properly *Homo,* then presently italicized provisional species of each whittle down to races. The fossil-finders and we are in the same business except that our men can be interviewed, blood-typed, set on a treadmill, and they answer back.

Taxonomy in *Homo* is not one game for the living and a relaxed set of rules for those legally dead. To sex a fossil, or infer a group, or to pronounce taxonomic difference, one must have proficiency of the same kind in those now alive. Processes of ongoing evolution extend backward as well as forward. While the focus in this book is on man now alive, the approaches, the problems, the search for evidence is not separated by any chasm. Many a problem of the fossil past can be resolved by looking at the present.

THE STUDY OF RACE

The real question, of course, is why we study race, why we are interested in raciation in man, and why we expend valuable time and considerable money in the investigation of such seemingly esoteric subjects as the blood groups of the Idaho Basques.

For some the existence of races is a challenge, as with mountains that beg to be climbed simply because they are there. In much the same vein, an isolated race, unsullied and unstudied, still beckons with romantic appeal. As with explorer Burton, there are always some who will brave dangers and risk their own fortunes to be the first to visit and describe a previously unstudied population.

Still others are interested in taxonomy, that is, classification. And to have a complete taxonomy, that is, a complete classification, all human populations must be seen and studied. We are far from a complete taxonomy for man: part of Africa, much of Asia and a surprising portion of South America is still to be investigated with care. In the meanwhile, new race-populations are springing up, and these too merit analysis.

Another reason for studying race is phylogenetic. How are races related to each other, and which races arose from others? In some cases we have historical data to guide us as with the Cape Colored, the American Colored, the Ladino and the neo-Hawaiian. Even so, serological data are necessary in order to complete our knowledge as to proportions entering into admixture. In other cases we own mere educated guesses. Clearly the American Indians stem from Asiatic Mongoloids, but when and where? Are the Bushmen ancient, going back to the earliest origins of Africa, or are they merely desert-adapted southerners? Conversely, are the Zulu and Bantu themselves evolved Bushmen?

These latter problems bring us to the more intriguing reasons for investigating race, including the question of how races and particular races came to be. Why are Negroes dark, and are there similar explanations for the peoples of Southern India and the Melanesian Islands? Why do Asiatics have straight, coarse black hair and sparse beards? Why are the Papago fatter than the Navajo in the same region? Why are the Basques so peculiar in their Rh blood group distribution? Why are the Pygmies pygmy, the Blackfoot Indians tall, and why are the Aleut short?

Why are certain genetic diseases limited to some groups and absent in others? Since such diseases are deleterious and subject to natural selection, what explains the continuance of sickle-cell disease in Africa, favism and Mediterranean anemia in Southern Europe, or Kuru in New Guinea? And turning from disease to physiology, are the Eskimo cold-adapted and are the natives of Dakar or Brazzaville adapted to both heat and high humidity as would be reasonable to suppose?

Such questions as these are no longer excursions into the unanswerable. Within the past decade we have seen some of them explained, and others close to understanding. How races came to be is no longer a philosopher's conundrum, and the peculiarities of particular races come closer and closer to comprehension. The distinctive characteristics of every race may now be understood in terms of the special environments in which they have lived.

The study of race bears a personal attractiveness to us. This is our species, and as men we are inevitably fascinated by man. Now, quite suddenly we are in a position, as many investigative fields come to maturity, to answer the fundamental questions that will lead to a more complete understanding of the different races of mankind.

SUGGESTED READINGS

Baker, P. T.: The biological race concept as a research tool. *Am. J. Phys. Anthropol., 27*:21-26, 1967.

Brace, C. L.: A nonracial approach towards the understanding of human diversity. In Montagu, A. (Ed.) : *The Concept of Race.* Glencoe, Free Press, 1964.

Buettner-Janusch, J.: *Origins of Man.* New York, John Wiley, 1966.

Comas, J.: Biological subdivisions of the Indian on the basis of physical anthropology. In *Biomedical Challenges Presented by the American Indian.* Pan American Health Organization, Washington, D.C., Scientific Publication No. 165, 1968.

Count, E. W.: *This Is Race.* New York, Shuman, 1950.

Dobzhansky, Th.: *Mankind Evolving.* New Haven, Yale University Press, 1962.

Dunn, L. C.: *Heredity and Evolution in Human Populations.* Cambridge, Harvard University Press, 1959.

*Garn, S. M. (Ed.) : *Readings on Race.* Springfield, Thomas, 1959, 1968.

Garn, S. M. (Ed.): *Culture and the Direction of Human Evolution.* Detroit, Wayne State University Press, 1964.

Gossett, T.: *Race: The History of an Idea in America.* Dallas, Southern Methodist University Press, 1963.

Hunt, E. E., Jr.: Anthropometry, genetics and racial history. *Am. Anthropol., 61*:64-87, 1959.

Kalmus, H.: *Genetics.* Harmondsworth, England, Penguin Books, 1950.

Lasker, G.: *The Evolution of Man.* New York, Holt, Reinhart and Winston, 1961.

Mason, P. (Ed.) : *Man, Race and Darwin.* London, Oxford University Press, 1960.

Montagu, A. (Ed.) : *The Concept of Race.* Glencoe, Free Press, 1964.

Montague, M. F. A.: *An Introduction to Physical Anthropology.* Springfield, Thomas, 1951, 1960.

The Race Question in Modern Science. UNESCO publications, New York, Morrow, 1956.

Thieme, F.: The population as a unit of study. *Am. Anthropol., 54:* 504-509, 1952.

Washburn, S. L.: Thinking about race. *Science Education, 28:*65-76, 1944.

---

*Suggested readings contained in *Readings on Race* are designated by an asterisk throughout this book.

II

GEOGRAPHICAL, LOCAL AND MICRO-RACES

RACE, "RACE" AND *RACE*

The original edition of *Races,* published in 1950, contained a listing of thirty living race-populations in man. In the very same year, in his *Genetics and the Races of Man,* William C. Boyd described a total of six races: however, one of them was both hypothetical and extinct. Though Boyd (1958) has more recently augmented his list of races, raising the number to thirteen, we are obviously dealing with different orders of magnitude.

Other listings of human races have run the numerical gamut. A century ago some workers divided mankind into but two races, a straight-haired race and a woolly-haired race. Most physical anthropologists have described from twenty to fifty distinct races, though some of these races refer to individual "types" and not to breeding populations. Specialists, working with particular areas of the world have been even more generous in their race-assignments, granting fifty or more for Europe alone (cf. Coon, 1950).

Faced with such a perplexing situation, such a range of numbers of races, it is customary to refer to "lumpers" and "splitters." Lumpers, among taxonomists, are those who group a number of distinct varieties into one broader, larger category, explaining that the differences are too trivial to warrant so complex a taxonomy. Splitters, on the other hand, take the microscopic rather than the macroscopic view holding that any distinct variety merits attention.

But the situation in regard to man is not simply a matter of lumping or splitting: rather it is due to an overly elastic use of the term *race.* For some workers, such as Boyd (1950), *races* are identical to geographically delimited collections of races. Practically, Boyd's "races" are identical with the "stocks," "divisions," "primary races," or "major races" as defined by previous workers.

To other human taxonomists, however, particularly those influenced by population genetics, a *race* is a *population*. Inevitably, therefore, equating "race" with population-collections results in a smaller number of races, while restricting the term race to actual populations results in a far larger number of races. It is as if the term *regiment* were variously employed to refer to platoons, squadrons, brigades, and armies.

One expedient would be to coin a new set of words for taxonomic units smaller than the species. One might have the *species,* then the *stock,* then the *breed,* then the *variety,* etc. But there are dangers in setting up a completely new terminology, as mentioned in the last chapter. The most practical suggestion is one made by Bernhold Rensch, the German systematist, in 1929. He uses the term *geographical race* to describe the broad, geographically delimited population collections, and the term *local race* to refer to race-populations themselves. As Ernst Mayr (1950) puts it, "this system facilitates communication without encumbering nomenclature."

While *geographical races* and *local races* adequately distinguish Bushmen, for example, from Africans in general, or Navahos or Hopi Indians from the broad category of Amerindians, these two terms are not quite enough to fit all of the data. The population of Oslo is genetically distinct from the population of Helsinki, yet neither is a true breeding population, a genetic isolate. Salerno and Padua are distinct in many respects, yet there is no fence about Salerno, and no moat surrounding Padua. Here Dobzhansky's term *microgeographical race* comes to our assistance in delineating statistically distinct populations which cannot be delimited as circumscribed breeding populations. However, and with apologies to Professor Dobzhansky, the term *micro-race* will be used throughout this book (instead of micro geographical race) simply because it is less confusing, less likely to be confounded with *geographical race.*

These terms, geographical races, local races, and micro-races, do not encumber nomenclature. Whosoever uses them is immediately aware of the fact that he is dealing with race, the taxonomic unit immediately below the species. These terms facilitate communication in that they explicitly state which taxonomic unit is involved. With respect to geographical races, there is no plethora of them. As race-collections they certainly do not exceed ten. Of local races there is obviously a multitude numbering surely into the hundreds. The Navajo, Hopi, Zuni, Pima, Papago, Cocopa, Haida, and Salish are but a few of the local races among the American Indians. And micro-races, in densely populated areas of Europe and Asia, run into the thousands, each hamlet being genetically somewhat distinct from the others.

Clearly, the one term race is not enough for us to use. By being more explicit we gain clarity and lose confusion.

GEOGRAPHICAL RACES

The *geographical race* is the largest of the three categories of races and encompasses (in each geographical region) the other two. A geographical race is by definition a geographically delimited collection of similar races (Fig. 3). To a large extent the

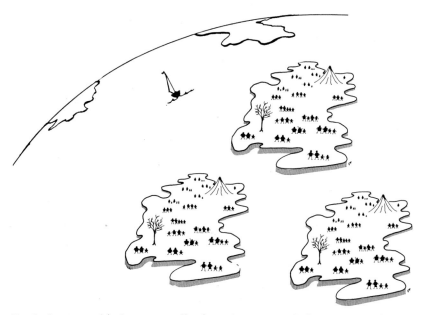

Fig. 3. A geographical race—a collection of race populations, separated from other such collections by major geographical barriers.

geographical races of mankind coincide with the major continents and are therefore identical with *continental* races, as the term is used by Boyd and others. However, geographical races may also be spread over major island chains, as is evident in the Pacific today.

The existence of geographical races is due, of course, to the great geographical barriers, chief among them oceans, that formerly limited the expansion and migration of local races and protected them from the introduction of different genes. Thus, in pre-Colonial South America, there was little or no gene-introduction from either Africa or the Pacific. Gene flow in and out of South America was funneled through the narrow isthmus of Central America. The great sub-continent of Australia also represents a situation where geographical race and geography coincide due to water barriers all around and no major tradition of navigation and sea travel.

However, the continents marked out in different colors on the map do not perfectly delimit geographical races, whereas the geographical barriers to human migration do. Africa is separated from Europe, and its own northern region, by great ranges of desert, scarcely inhabited by a few wandering tribes, and by the Atlas mountains. South of the Sahara and through Africa to its southernmost tip there is one geographical race, comprising a very large number of local races, whereas North Africa is racially confluent with the Near East and Europe.

Similarly, the eastern limit to the geographical race inhabiting Europe is in Western Asia, in the scarcely inhabited uplands, and not coincident with conventional continental divisions. However, the high and uninviting mountains that mark the Tibeto-Indian border on the maps have long restricted population interchange to a thin trickle. The facts of geography, the mountain ranges, the deserts, and the oceans have made geographical races by fencing them in.

Within each geographical race the individual populations resemble each other more or less. In the aggregate, resemblances within geographical races are far greater than those between them. However, intra-population differences are still great, especially taken trait by trait or gene by gene. In each geographical race there are tall populations and short populations, heavy-set groups and linear groups. Certain human differences transcend geographical race and are more meaningfully distributed with respect to climate or disease (Ch. VII).

A geographical race is a collection of populations whose similarities are due to long-continued confinement within set geographical limits.

LOCAL RACES

In contrast to geographical races which are geographically delimited population collections, *local races* correspond more nearly to the breeding populations themselves. Whether isolated by distance, by geographical barriers or by social prohibitions, local races are totally or largely endogamous, and the very small amount of gene-flow ordinarily comes from contiguous and related local races (Fig. 4.).

The Bushmen of South Africa are one example of a local race where the territorial limits are defined and where breeding has been confined almost exclusively to the local race itself. The several native local races of Australia also typify the situation, as do the Ituri-forest Pygmies. Though the latter have contributed wives to the taller Negroes around them, gene-flow appears to be largely one-way, and the Ituri-forest Pygmies constitute a true breeding population to the present day.

Clear-cut local races such as these are largely independent evolutionary units and as such are of particular interest. Other examples of local races include the Yemenite Jews, isolated reproductively from their Arab neighbors and from other Jewish populations for millennia. Whereas the Yemenite Jews, now being absorbed into the Europeanized population of Israel, have religious affinities with the European, North African, Kurdistani and Oriental Jews, their status as a separate local race held for thousands of years.

As a further example of local races, one may consider the various Eskimo populations widely spread from Greenland across the Arctic to Alaska, the Aleutians, and Siberia. Each has been sepa-

Fig. 4. A local race—a breeding population adapted to local selection pressures and maintained by either natural or social barriers to gene interchange.

rated from the other for millennia. It is questionable whether one Greenland Eskimo got to Alaska in the last five hundred years. As to the Aleut, despite their proximity to Alaska, well under 1 per cent of Alaskan genes have found their recent way into Umnak, Atka, or the Pribilofs.

Local races are most easily identified where populations are relatively small and there is little doubt as to their limits as indicated by geographical separation or by cultural prohibitions on marriage outside of the group, as with the several Gypsy populations of Europe. Local races can also be delineated, though less neatly in the populous areas of the world. By way of example, the demographic populations of Northwestern Europe and Southern Europe share markedly different histories and are, on the whole, quite distinct. The former population, relatively late to expand, has done so following the discovery of the New World and the subcontinents of the Pacific and has poured into these territories. Thus it is that North America, New Zealand, and Australia constitute territorial extensions of Northwestern Europe from a racial point of view, while Central and South America is more of an extension of the breeding population of Southern Europe.

The Northwest Europeans, though constituting a smaller taxonomic unit than the European Geographical Race, are not as neat a population as those mentioned earlier in this section. Numerous special problems interpose themselves, the problem of differential migration (who migrated?) and differential selection in the new and at least temporarily hostile environments. Moreover, even among the stay-at-homes, there are local differences, as shall be mentioned shortly under micro-races.

Nevertheless, it is the local race that we view and measure somewhat more easily when the numbers are small, whereas the geographical race represents more of an abstraction. The population as a unit of study is identical with the local race and becomes increasingly more difficult to investigate as it becomes less easy to delineate.

MICRO-RACES

For much of the world today, as in Europe and Eastern Asia, neat local races are hard to come by. Except for a few populations in Europe such as the Basques, or the Lapps, one cannot define a local race by an ethnographic survey. A man from Berlin marries a woman from Stuttgart, her brother lives in Hamburg and has married a Dane from Copenhagen, whose sister now resides in the Finnish University city of Turku (but is on leave in Cleveland).

Nevertheless, there are very real differences in the genetic makeup of cities and continual changes in the frequencies of various genes in either the north-south or the east-west direction. Some of the differences are so apparent that we can divide Europe into a series of local races—Northwest European, East Baltic, Alpine, Mediterranean, etc. Other differences are more subtle, visible to the trained observer, or detectable by the serologist or biochemist from his data.

Regional differences in Europe are in part due to ancient settlement patterns and to the local perseverance of local races. Even though the genetic insularity of the old city-states has long been breached, propinquity is still a very real determinant of mating. "International" marriages, especially in the academic and professional classes, should not blind us to the fact that marriage, or mating, is a mathematical function of distance. With millions of potential mates, the male ordinarily choses one near at hand. In fact, there is a third kind of genetic isolation. In addition to geographical isolation, as between continents, and cultural isolation, as between local races, there is isolation by numbers. The denser the population, the more nearly the boy marries the girl next door (Fig. 5).

This latter phenomenon, which somewhat deflates the picture of the romantic human male and allies him more nearly with the field mouse or mosquito (which have similar mating ranges), has the effect of maintaining micro-races. It will be eons, at the present rate, before Copenhagen is no longer different, genetically, from Oslo or Stockholm, or Venice from Naples or Rome. Furthermore, local selective factors will continue to be at work. Thus, one genotype will be favored in this city and another in that, maintaining and even exaggerating the genetical differences that now exist between micro-races.

TAXONOMY AND RESEARCH ON RACE

Given geographical races, local races and micro-races, there may appear to be some question as to their relative importance. From one point of view, geographical races may seem to be of greatest interest. Geographical races are large, and there are so few of them. From another point of view local races may be favored. After all, local races are natural populations (not collections of convenience); they are the basic evolutionary units, and they can be studied in divers ways.

Actually, the importance of these successive taxonomic categories depends very much on the problem at hand. By way of

Fig. 5. Micro-races. In a densely populated area local races may not be demonstrable, yet biological distance may maintain regional differences as in the centers A, B, and C shown here.

example, the ancestry of the American Indians and their relationship to Asiatics focuses attention on two geographical races. Differences between Europeans and Asiatics with respect to blood group B, the Diego factor, or the Rhesus-negative gene again involve geographical races. The Polynesians and possible explanations for their polymorphism necessitate attention to contiguous geographical races in Asia, in Melanesia and Papua, and in Australia.

At the same time, the diversity of populations within each geographical race introduces problems of its own. If we are to compare Amerindians to Asiatics, with an interest in common origins, which Amerindians and what Asiatics shall we compare? Shall we use weighted average values which may be biased by particular populations, or try to select prototypical Amerindians and Asiatics in which case our comparisons obviously reflect the populations selected for use?

In contrast to geographical races, local races are both easier to define and simpler to investigate. Within the course of a year it is possible to measure and blood-type all living Aleut. It is possible to obtain a fair sample of all known Bushman bands. Moreover, with local races, we are interested in local selective factors; diet, disease, and environmental stresses. Local races, therefore, commend themselves to the investigation of evolutionary forces. The degree of out-marriage can be determined in assaying the role of "drift." Survivors can be studied to determine possible directions of selection. With local races inhabiting a fixed territory, and where their neighbors can be examined as well, the role of admixture may be quantified. Local races, therefore, offer the maximum opportunity for evolutionary studies.

With micro-races, our human material approaches more nearly the demographic population rather than the natural or race-population. Micro-races are not delimited by geographical or even tribal barriers to gene flow. Nevertheless micro-races offer numerous opportunities to investigate the mechanisms of differentiation. In Saudi-Arabia, as in the more populous parts of Africa, the incidence of malarial infestation may be related to local differences in the frequency of the sickle-cell gene. In European cities it is possible to investigate differential survival in the face of smog, a problem we have begun to consider in Donora, Pennsylvania, Los Angeles, and other American communities. Differential mortality and morbidity brings about genetic changes within populations, and micro-races offer the best opportunities at present for such comparative studies.

With respect to geographical races, local races, and micro-races, the question is not which is more important, but rather what questions we are trying to answer.

SUMMARY

The number of races of mankind, which varies from no more than two to many hundred according to the taxonomy consulted, ceases to pose a major problem if the taxonomic category used is precisely defined.

Immediately below the species is the *geographical race,* a geographically delimited collection of local races which may differ markedly, one from the other. *Local races,* in turn, correspond to natural or breeding populations and are at once the units of evolutionary change and the common subjects for investigation. *Micro-races,* though not isolated geographically or by extensive cultural prohibitions, still differ from each other in numerous ways.

Geographical races, local races, and micro-races offer opportunities for very different investigations in relation to race. One is not more real or more fundamental than the other, but each provides the answer to different questions and the solution to different problems of ongoing evolution in man.

SUGGESTED READINGS

Boyd, W. C.: *Genetics and the Races of Man.* Boston, Little, Brown and Company, 1950.

*Boyd, W. C.: *Genetics and the Races of Man.* Boston University Lecture. Boston, Boston University Press, 1958.

Coon, C. S.: *Races of Europe.* New York, Macmillan, 1939.

Coon, C. S., Garn, S. M. and Birdsell, J. B.: *Races. A Study of the Problems of Race Formation in Man.* Springfield, Thomas, 1950.

Dobzhansky, Th.: *Genetics and the Origin of Species.* New York, Columbia University Press, 1954, Ch. VI.

*Garn, S. M. and Coon, C. S.: On the number of races of mankind. *Am. Anthropol.,* 57:996-1001, 1955.

Gossett, T. F.: *Race: The History of an Idea in America.* Dallas, Southern Methodist University Press, 1963.

Laughlin, W. S.: Races of mankind: Continental and local. *Anthropological Papers of the University of Alaska,* 8:89-99, 1960.

Mayr, E.: Taxonomic categories in fossil hominids. *Cold Spring Harbor Symposia on Quantitative Biology,* 15:109-118, Cold Spring Harbor, The Biological Laboratory, 1950.

Rensch, B.: *Daz Prinzip geographischer Rassenkreise und das Problem der Artbildung.* Berlin, Boentraeger, 1929.

---

*Reprinted in *Readings on Race.*

Rensch, B.: *Evolution Above the Species Level.* New York, Columbia University Press, 1960.

Simpson, G. C.: *Principles of Taxonomy.* New York, Columbia University Press, 1961.

III

RACE DIFFERENCES

R<small>ACES DIFFER</small> in a great many respects—in language, in dress, in gesture, in body size and proportions, in amino acid excretion patterns, in tooth morphology, and in the proportions (or frequencies) of the various blood groups.

Those differences that are primarily learned, such as language or religion, may play an important role in maintaining the genetic isolates we call races. Languages are effective isolating mechanisms, as are religions. In various parts of the world there are *sympatric races,* occupying the same territory, but reproductively isolated because of religious practices or language differences. Yet, such learned differences in behavior are not biologically inherited: they may be concommitants of race, but are not a part of race.

Besides such learned differences between races, clearly nongenic in nature, there are many differences in body size and form that are responsive to environmental alterations. Stature is a type example. Though stature is in part inherited, nutritional adequacy during growth affects stature to a very large degree. Headform, once considered a purely inherited trait has since been included among the "plastic" human features, susceptible to nutritional modification or to the effects of cradling and other skull-deforming practices. Such plastic traits, though showing considerable differences from population to population, are of questionable utility in racial comparison except when great caution has been used in untangling the effects of nurture from genetic nature.

The ideal traits for use in racial comparisons and in the analysis of ongoing evolution within races are those that are simply inherited and of known mode of inheritance. With such traits it is possible to go beyond *trait frequencies* (the proportion of individuals showing the traits in question) to *gene frequencies* (the proportion of the allelic genes in question).* Gene frequencies, though mathematically derived from trait frequencies, make for more accurate comparisons and facilitate calculations. That is why the blood groups, the haptoglobins, taste-blindness, the abnormal hemoglobins, fingerprints, and rare hereditary diseases are so useful in the study of race: knowing the mode of inheritance, phenotype (or trait) frequencies can be supplanted by gene frequencies.

Nevertheless, there are many racial differences, not simply inherited, but due to the cumulative effect of several genes, that are of marked utility in population comparisons. Such "polygenic" traits include hair form and skin pigmentation (excepting albinism), tooth form, and the extremes of body build. Not knowing the mode of inheritance, gene frequencies cannot be calculated and the mathematics of population comparisons is therefore hampered.

A further caution must be added about purely phenotypic differences, even if clearly inheritable. A given phenotype may be due to one set of genes in one population and another set of genes in a second population. It is by no means certain that the genes for dark skin are the same in all populations and therefore the assumption of genetic affinity between the dark-skinned peoples of Africa and Melanesia is questionable. This caution applies with even greater force to such complex phenotypes as nose form or the extremes of stature. It is questionable whether the various "pygmies" of the world are related simply because they are pygmy, and it is a very tenuous assumption that the Ainu are related to Europeans simply because of their generalized hirsutism.

Thus it is that the neatly and simply inherited differences are currently of maximum use in the study of race, While other obviously inheritable but polygenic traits are of secondary utility until more is known about their genetics and the appropriate mathematical methods have been developed.

---

*Individuals of blood type O are homozygous for the gene, being of the genotype OO. But the majority of individuals of blood type A or B are of the genotype OA or OB. The gene frequency for O is therefore greater than the trait frequency. In the case of Mendelian dominants the situation is reversed. For computational methods see Boyd (1950) appendix A.

PIGMENTATION AND RACE

Nevertheless, racial differences in skin pigmentation deserve first mention, if only because such differences have been long observed. Among the lightest-skinned individuals of northern Europe there is little of the brown-black pigment called *melanin* in the lower layers of the skin, and the apparent color of the skin is largely due to reflections from the skin surface, with some of the blood pigments showing through. So-called "whites," of course are not white at all, but a light pinkish brown, reflecting from less than 20 per cent of the light (in the blue end of the spectrum) to nearly 40 per cent in the fairest. The "browns" and "blacks" have increasing amounts of melanin, and in the darkest skins, no more than 1 per cent of the light may be reflected from the unexposed skin areas. Skin cancer goes with light skins and exposure.

To the best of our knowledge, skin pigmentation is primarily dark melanin in various amounts and in various degrees of dispersion. There are also yellow and yellow-red *pheomelanins*, but not known for man except perhaps in red hair follicles. At any rate there is no true yellow-skinned race and we need not invent a complicated ancestry for the Bushmen who have been described as having "yellowish" skins.

The amount of pigment in the unexposed skin, of course, is only half of the story, for the capacity to tan is also important, and this capacity is not invariably related to the unexposed skin color. Very little has been done on this tanning capacity, but it figures large in racial appearances. A well-tanned Norwegian or Swede may be darker than an indoor-working American Negro. The light skins of aristocratic Polynesians or Arabs need not be indicative of genetic differences but merely differential exposure to sunlight. On the other hand, the capacity to tan may be limited in even brunette-skinned individauls. Therefore racial comparisons must be limited to areas of skin ordinarily unexposed to the sun's rays or made in connection with controlled tanning studies.

THE HAIR

Next to the skin and its pigmentation, hair form, color, and abundance have been most often utilized in racial taxonomies.

In fact, hair form alone would effectively discriminate two-thirds of the world's populations.

The range of hair forms is wide, and in this respect, man is more variable than any other primate, though in all fairness no other primate occupies so wide a geographical range! In much of Asia and in aboriginal America, the head hair is straight or nearly so and coarse (over 100 microns). In much of Africa head hair is highly curved, even to the tight centimeter-wide spirals best seen in the Bushmen and Hottentot. In Europe there is a wide range of hair forms, from nearly straight—but rarely of Mongoloid coarseness—to helical, as seen in Greek statues of Pericles' time. A world survey of head-hair form is given below.

WORLD DISTRIBUTION OF HAIR FORMS
(By Geographical Areas)

Geographical Area	Straight Coarse	Straight to Wavy	Helical to "Woolly"	Spiral Tuft
North and South America	X	X		
Polynesia	X	X	X	
Australia		X	?	
Papua—New Guinea		X	X	
Asia	X	X		
India		X	X	(?)
Africa		X	X	X
Europe		X	X	

Hair on the body, less extensively studied, is characterized by great racial variability. In most of Asia, America, and much of Africa, body hair is sparse or absent. In Europe, and the Middle East to Afghanistan and Pakistan, body hair is often well-developed. Sporadically, generalized hirsutism exists—in Papua and New Guinea, among the Australian aborigines, and in the Ainu of northern Japan. However, the hairiness of the Ainu has been exaggerated as a brief stay at any American bathing beach will confirm.

Balding, to be more exact, male pattern balding constitutes a very real racial difference. Hormone-mediated and gene-determined, it is rare among Asiatics, Amerindians and Africans, and common in Europe and the Middle East. Balding is associated with, but genetically independent of generalized hirsutism. At its extreme manifestation, male pattern balding begins in the early twenties. Possibly, if Italian data hold for other countries, early male pattern balding is associated with increased fertility. One study relates male pattern balding to the sex ratio.

THE BONES

Racial differences in the size, proportions, form, and mineral content of the bones are well documented for a number of groups, since these variations have been extensively studied on skeletons.

Using trunk-length as a reference, the relative proportions of the limb bones vary markedly from Eskimo and Japanese, at one extreme, to American Negroes and especially certain African groups at the other extreme. Racial differences in the relative lengths of the metatarsal bones of the feet as expressed by differing digital formulae are obvious even in the living, as are racial differences in the calcaneus and astragalus.

The presence of accessory or "Wormian" bones along the suture lines of the skull, typically between the occipital and parietal bones where they meet at the back of the head, is characteristic of Asiatics and especially American Indians (Fig. 24). This alone is a great help to law-enforcement officers when presented with an exhumed skeleton to identify. Accessory or suture bones distinguish recent white burials from older Amerindian remains.

Medically, Negro-white differences in the volume of the sacral canal become of importance when certain types of spinal anasthesia are contemplated. Racial differences in the architecture of the pelvic bones are often so marked as to make identification possible from the pelvis alone.

Recent studies on bone density reveal marked racial differences. The weight-to-volume ratio is higher in Negro skeletons and it appears that Negro boys and girls have higher mineral requirements for growth (Garn, 1970). In contrast, the thickness of cortical bone is less in subjects of Chinese and Japanese origin, whether born in the United States or born and reared in Asia (Garn, Pao, and Rihl, 1964). Total bone apposition is greater in Negro subjects in the United States, even those from undernourished rural areas of the South. In consequence, during the period of adult bone loss (osteoporosis) women of African origin experience fewer femoral and radial fractures. Such differences in the rates of bone formation and bone resorption have practical importance, especially after age 40 when progressive bone loss increases the probability of fracture.

THE VARIABLE DENTITION

Many racial differences in the dentition are known and documented, due (in part) to the fact that the teeth are equally accessible to study in the living and in skeletal collections as well. Teeth can be investigated in the living mouth, directly or by x-ray, or after extraction, or in the form of plaster casts from plastic "impressions," or in archeological museum specimens.

Tooth size varies considerably from population to population. Crown size, for example, is largest in Australian aborigines, New Guinea natives, and Pima Indians and smallest in Lapps, African Bushmen, Cochin (India), and Yemenite Jews. The largest-toothed living populations approach or even exceed Neanderthal ranges (see Ch. XIV). Root length, which differs between the sexes, is also a racial variant, being especially short in some Asiatic populations.

Taking crown size of all twenty-eight permanent teeth (save M3) into account, it is possible to construct a crown-size profile pattern which illustrates taxonomic relationships, as well as the profound patterned differences from one population to the next. Closely related groups (like two series of Japanese or Cochin and Yemenite Jews) have very similar tooth-size profile patterns. Expectably, Aleutian Aleut resemble both Greenland Eskimos and Japanese to some extent (cf. Garn, Lewis, and Walenga, 1968). But Swedes and Lapps, though geographically contiguous, prove remarkably unalike in the crown-size profile pattern.

Differences also exist in the *relative* size of the different teeth —incisors, canines, premolars, and molars. In some groups the anterior teeth are exceptionally large, in others they are relatively small. Parts of the dental complement are separately inheritable. So the patterning of tooth size offers unique opportunities to make comparisons in a single polymorphic tissue system.

The form of the teeth offers many examples of differences as well. For example, the back surfaces of the incisors are "shovel-shaped" in many American Indians (see Fig. 7) and, to a lesser extent, in Polynesians and some Finns and in many of the classic fossil hominids. The number of cusps on the molar teeth varies too, being most often reduced in Middle-Eastern groups and increased in number in some of the Melanesian and Australian groups. Cusp number and tooth size are partially related, as is the relative number of cusps on M1 and M2 and the relative crown sizes of these two molar teeth.

Agenesis (congenital absence) of teeth varies from group to group. The third molar, M3, is rarely absent in East and West Africans, it is lacking in about 12 per cent of Europeans, and in 30 per cent or more of some Amerindian, Eskimo, and Asiatic groups. Along with third molar agenesis goes agenesis or size reduction of I2 and M2, and size reduction of the remaining teeth. Tooth size, tooth number, cusp number, and tooth-size patterning go together, as does the "canine field" of tooth size and sexual dimorphism, affecting I2, C and P1 as a cluster or "field."

Other dental variants include Carabelli's molar cusp (found in the deciduous and the permanent molars—see Fig. 6), relative size of the pulp chamber in the molar teeth, and differences in the timing of tooth eruption and in the sequence or order of tooth eruption. Though tooth calcification and movement are slightly affected by the nutritional state, tooth formation and tooth movement rates are to the larger extent genetically determined. So Aleutian Aleut boys and girls are markedly ahead of Boston boys and girls in tooth eruption. East African boys may be phenomenally advanced in third molar eruption, as early as the thirteenth year.

While the nutritional status, including available fluorine, cannot be neglected, the bulk of tooth-size variance, and that of crown morphology, cusp number, and tooth number reduction has a genetic basis. Through casts, radiographs, and *in vivo* measurements, racial differences in the dentition are rather easily studied.

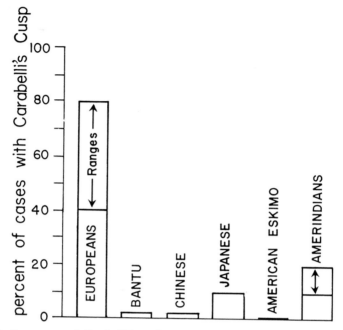

Fig. 6. Frequency of Carabelli's molar cusp in different geographical groups. Europeans tend to have maximum frequencies of this accessory cusp, which is least common in Eskimo, Bantu, and Chinese. (Data taken from Carbonell, V. M.: The tubercle of Carabelli in the Kish dentition. *J. Dent. Res., 39:* 124-128, 1960.)

GROWTH AND RACE

Since the rate of growth and the timing of maturation are both greatly affected by caloric and nutrient intake, definite statements about racial differences in growth were long hard to make. The old notion that Southern Europeans matured earlier proved wrong, in fact, and only the best-fed or even overfed Polynesians were at par with middle-class Americans of European origin when the timing of menarche or other measures of sexual maturation was taken into account.

Nevertheless, some racial differences in growth rate and maturational timing do emerge. By way of example, the prenatal growth of the leg bones is greater in American Negro foetuses, less in Americans of European origin, and least in those of Japan-

SHOVEL-SHAPED INCISORS
IN AMERICAN INDIANS

 REDUCED COMPACT (CORTICAL)
BONE IN ASIATICS

SPIRAL-TUFT HEAD-
HAIR IN AFRICANS

 "INNER" EYEFOLDS IN
ASIATICS AND AMERICAN
INDIANS

THE POST-
AREOLAR CONSTRICTION
IN MICRONESIAN
WOMEN

Fig. 7. Five areas of racial differentiation. (1) Shovel-shaping of the incisors attains a maximum degree of expression in American Indians. (2) Chinese and Japanese exhibit reduced compact bone, even on adequate calcium intake. (3) Spiral-tuft head hair, common in Africa, reaches its extremes in Bushman and Hottentot populations. (4) The "inner" eyefold, covering the inner margin of the eye and the caruncula, is responsible for the half-moon, slant-eye of many Asiatic and Amerindian peoples. (5) The postareolar constriction of the breast is particularly common in Micronesian women but may occasionally be observed in Bantu populations.

ese ancestry, as Adolph Schultz (1926) was first to show. Postnatally, certain of the bony nuclei are earlier to appear in American Negro infants, and this appears to be true in Africa as well, as Geber pointed out in *Courrier* in 1956 and in *Pediatrics* in 1957. Other groups, such as Hong Kong Chinese appear to be earlier in the early-appearing centers of the hand and wrist, but later in the later-appearing centers, a progressive delay that may be of nutritional origin, according to the work of Marjorie Lee, now at the University of Nebraska.

The order in which postnatal bony nuclei ("ossification centers") appear, is genetically determined in large part, and it is therefore not surprising that sequences and some sequence reversals are somewhat different in Guatemalan Indians, in Quechua-speaking Indians of Peru, and Indians from the Equadorian highlands. Malnutrition and protein-calorie malnutrition delays ossification timing, but not ossification sequence, so sequence can be studied in survey programs in different population samples.

For the teeth, the data appear to be considerable. Tooth eruption, slightly affected by nutritional status, is often earlier in Navajo, Mayan Indian, Formosan, Aleut, and American Negro children than in recent U.S.A. and U.K. norms. Third molar eruption, rare in adolescents of European ancestry before ages 17 to 20, may occur by age 13 in boys from Kenya.

Growth and size and form are complicated. As nutrition improves and disease is controlled, growth is greater, maturation is earlier, and body proportions change. Within this changing matrix of development, sequence differences and patterned differences can be demonstrated on a family-line basis and between populations, and sequences rare in one genetic population may be common in another.

BRACHYMESOPHALANGIA AND CONE-SHAPED EPIPHYSES

Brachymesophalangia ("broad middle phalanges") shown in Figure 8 is a minor, genetically determined hand variant ranging from rare (under 1%) to common (over 10%) in different populations. In slightly less than 1 per cent of American Negro, American White, and Iranian subjects the middle segment of the little finger is shortened and broadened. In Mexican-Americans in Texas the trait frequency is about 4%, it is 3% or so in Guatemala and Equador, and it is reportedly more common still in Japanese from Hiroshima and Nagasaki. Along with brachy-

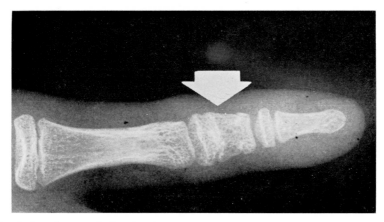

Fig. 8. Brachymesophalangia (broad middle phalanx) of the 5th digit here shown with a "cone-shaped" epiphysis. The short-broad digital segment is associated with size reduction of adjacent tubular bones of the hand and is far more common in American Indians and in Japanese and Chinese than in groups of European or African origin.

mesophalangia-5 goes reduction of the proximal and distal segments, the fifth metacarpal and the middle segment of the fourth finger (Garn, Fels, and Israel, 1967). So brachymesophalangia-5 demonstrates a "field" effect, much of the hand is involved and where the trait frequency is 2% or greater, Asiatic origins may be suspected.

BRACHYMESOPHALANGIA-5 IN 12 POPULATIONS

Population Studied	No.	Affected No.	Percent
Ohio	647	4	0.6
American Negroes	9094	43	0.5
Iran	226	2	0.9
Costa Rica	1841	23	1.3
Nicaragua	1722	33	1.9
El Salvador	1774	35	2.0
Guatemala	2700	93	3.4
Equador	182	6	3.3
Navajo	291	14	4.8
Mexican-Americans	2133	117	5.5
Peru	238	12	5.0
Hong Kong	247	12	5.0

From Garn, Fels, and Israel (1967), and Garn, Frisancho, and Poznanski (unpublished), 1970.

Along with brachymesophalangia-5 goes cone-shaped epiphyses. In about 33 per cent of such subjects, the epiphysis of mid-5 is cone-shaped or peg-shaped. The diaphysis has a pit or "crater" as shown in the illustration, and epiphyseal union may be premature. Cone-shaped epiphyses may be seen on other fingers, the first, the second and others, and cone-shaped epiphyses are remarkably common in Japanese, according to a review by K. P. Hertzog *et al.* (1968). Indeed, short fingers, brachymesophalangia, and cone-shaped epiphyses go together, though not perfectly.

Easily studied in hand radiographs at all ages, brachymesophalangia is an increasingly useful trait for racial comparisons.

FUSED CARPAL BONES

The seven oddly-shaped "round" bones of the wrist are ordinarily separate anatomical units. The hamate, capitate, trapezoid, and trapezium are separate in the distal row (adjacent to the metacarpals) and the triquetral, lunate, and scaphoid are separate

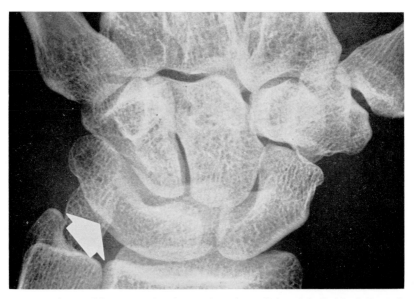

Fig. 9. Triquetral-lunate *fusion* in an American Colored individual. Rare in subjects of European origin, this carpal fusion is found in over 1 per cent of subjects of African ancestry and in as much as 6 per cent of subjects in some parts of Africa.

bones in the proximal row. Adjacent carpal centers may "fuse," however, and both the type and the frequency of genetically determined carpal fusion exhibit major racial differences.

The capitate and the hamate bones are fused in approximately 1 out of every 1,000 subjects of European origin and the frequency is approximately the same in American Negro subjects studied in the course of the National Nutrition Survey in 1968-1970. The capitate-trapezoid fusion is approximately as often fused in American subjects of European origin, but less frequently in American Negroes (see table).

THE DIFFERENTIAL FREQUENCY OF CARPAL FUSIONS

Fusion	*1589 Mexican-Americans*	*11,663 American Whites*	*7543 American Negroes*
Capitate-hamate	0.00	0.03	0.08
Capitate-trapezoid	0.00	0.03	0.01
Trapezoid-trapezium	0.00	0.03	0.03
Triquetral-lunate	0.06	0.10	1.58

Subjects three years of age and older (Garn, Poznanski, and Frisancho, unpublished).

The major difference is in the frequency of triquetral-lunate fusions which are far more frequent in the American Negroes. Indeed, the triquetral-lunate type of carpal fusion is approximately fifteen times as frequent in Americans of largely African origin with frequencies of close to 16 per 1,000.

Comparable radiographic studies in Africa indicate triquetral-lunate frequencies of 10 per 1,000, 20 per 1,000, and even as high as 60 per 1,000 in some groups (cf. O'Rahilly, 1957, and Cockshott, 1963). So the triquetral-lunate fusion clearly has an African locus and in reasonable consequence there is a much higher frequency in American Negroes and in Puerto Ricans.

PHYSIOLOGICAL AND BIOCHEMICAL DIFFERENCES

Investigations in human physiology and biochemistry have suggested many racial differences, most related to diet and way of life. Thus, "natives" tend to have low blood pressures and low blood cholesterol levels compared to Europeans, but blood pressures, cholesterols, and uric acid levels climb to European standards following urbanization, overeating, and underexercising.

There is evidence that South African natives have low 17-ketosteroid excretion rates, both in Africa and London, as described by Barnicot and Wolffson (1952). But the absence of balding need not be attributed to limited 17-ketosteroid secretion. J. B. Hamilton (1951) showed, in American Indians, that men who do not become bald have hair follicles resistant to hormonal stress, an example of "target-organ insensitivity."

Many individual differences in urinary excretion patterns are known, some of them "inborn errors of metabolism," as with alkaptonuria, maple-sugar urine, and PKU. One normal urinary constituent, however, shows most interesting individual and racial variations in amount excreted. The nonprotein amino acid β-aminoisobutyric acid is rarely excreted in large amounts by Australian aborigines or Europeans. However, a fair proportion of Chinese and Japanese excrete high amounts of β-AIB (see Fig. 8); this is true of many American Indian groups both native and mixed (Lasker, Mast and Tashian, 1969) and in Micronesia (Blumburg and Gartler, 1961). Without question, high levels of β-AIB excretion are suggestive of Asiatic affinities, though some of the data from both the Americas indicate far higher frequencies of high excretors in Central and South America than in the United States and Canada.

Now all evidence indicates that β-AIB excretion is controlled by a single gene and a recessive gene at that. Family-line studies are in accord with the suggestion that high excretors are homozygous recessives and that moderate excretors are heterozygotes. Even though β-AIB excretion is increased in pregnancy and though it varies through the menstrual cycle, the genetic evidence and the population distributions together make β-AIB polymorphism of major taxonomic interest. Though, at present, no adaptive significance can be attached either to the presence or absence of the recessive gene, recent studies in Japan suggest either prezygotic or prenatal selection, since there is an excess of excretor progeny from excretor-mother, nonexcretor-father pairings. And, of course, the possibility exists that selection is effected through the alternate metabolic pathway from β-AIB.

As Lasker, Mast, and Tashian put it, "Despite difficulties of collection and transportation, β-AIB and the neutral amino acids are apparently stable enough and indicative enough of an underlying polymorphism to give potentially useful information concerning mixed populations."

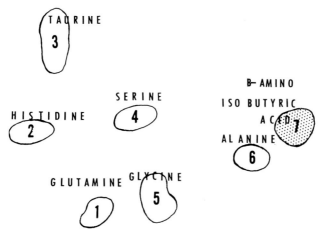

Fig. 10. Locations of various amino acids in the urinary chromatogram pictured in the frontispiece. The shaded area, No. 7, is occupied by β-AIB (β-aminoisobutyric acid). High β-AIB excretion levels in adults are common in Micronesia and moderately common on mainland Asia and in aboriginal America (see Blumberg and Gartler, 1961).

THE Gm ALLOTYPES: BACK TO CONVENTIONAL TAXONOMY?

Next to the ABO, MNS-U, Rh, Kell, Kidd, Diego, and Duffy blood groups, the Gm allotypes show greatest geographical differentiation. Indeed, when the full range of possibilities is taken into account they are practically diagnostic. There are Gm alleles peculiar to the Bushmen, others peculiar to Ainu, still others characteristic of Melanesians who speak one language group and still another set characteristic of Melanesians who speak another.

The Gm antigens are genetically determined, they are inherited usually as groups and individual numbered antigens such as Gm(3) and Gm(4) (5) and (12) and (10) and (13) are not necessarily different. The determinants are on the gamma-globulin molecule along with the Inv system but independent of it. At the present stage of testing, the Gm alleles or more correctly the Gm *phenogroups* elicited depend on the particular antigens used and so earlier population reports will not correspond to the most recent data given below.

Population or Sample	Gm Phenogroups			
Europeans and East Asiatics	$Gm^{1,17,21}$	$Gm^{1,2,17,21}$	$Gm^{3,5,13,14}$	
Ainu	$Gm^{1,17,21}$	$Gm^{1,2,17,21}$	$Gm^{1,13,17}$	$Gm^{2,17,21}$
Asiatics and American Indians	$Gm^{1,17,21}$	$Gm^{1,2,17,21}$	$Gm^{1,13,17}$	$Gm^{1,3,5,13,14}$
Micronesians	$Gm^{1,3,5,13,14}$	$Gm^{1,17,21}$		
New Guinea	$Gm^{1,3,5,13,14}$	$Gm^{1,5,13,14,17}$	$Gm^{1,2,17,21}$	$Gm^{1,17,21}$
	$Gm^{1,17,21}$			
Bougainville	$Gm^{1,3,5,13,14}$	$Gm^{1,2,17,21}$	$Gm^{1,17,21}$	
African and American Negroes	$Gm^{1,5,13,14,17}$	$Gm^{1,5,14,17}$	$Gm^{1,5,6,17}$	$Gm^{1,5,6,14,17}$
Pygmies	$Gm^{1,5,6,17}$	$Gm^{1,5,13,14,17}$		
Bushmen	$Gm^{1,17,21}$	$Gm^{1,5,17}$	$Gm^{1,13,17}$	$Gm^{1,5,13,14,17}$

From Steinberg, A. G. in *Annual Review of Genetics, 3*:25-52, 1969.

As things now stand, Steinberg feels that there is sufficient evidence from the Gm phenogroups to assign the Ainu to a unique status of their own (Ainu), to differentiate Bushmen and Hottentot from other peoples south of the Sahara, to distinguish Pygmies as having taxonomic identity of their own and in differentiating Austronesian and non-Austronesian language speakers in Oceania. With more antigens tested for, the Gm allegroups produce results more nearly comparable to conventional taxonomies.

THE HAPTOGLOBINS

The haptoglobins, symbolized by Hp, are globulin fractions that bind free hemoglobin. There are two common haptoglobin genes, Hp^1 and Hp^2, which singly and together produce the three distinct haptoglobin phenotypes Hp 1-1, Hp 2-1, and Hp 2-2, as pictured in Figure 11 on the opposite page. Besides Hp^1 and Hp^2, there is a third and far less common haptoglobin gene, Hp^{2m} (haptoglobin 2-modified), responsible for a phenotypically different pattern that is geographically circumscribed.

The Hp^1 gene is least common in Asia, with a gene frequency of 0.2 to 0.3. Thus the frequency of Hp^1 in Japan is 0.28 and slightly over 50 per cent of Japanese are, in consequence, of the Hp 2-2 phenotype (Steinberg and Matsumoto, 1964). The frequency of Hp^1 is somewhat higher in Europe, up to 0.4 or so.

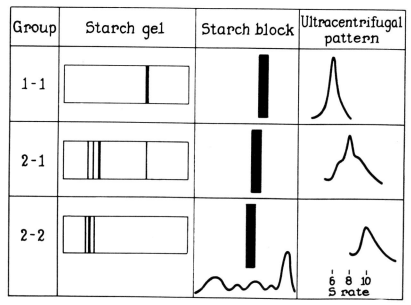

Fig. 11. The three haptoglobin phenotypes Hp 1-1, Hp 2-1, and Hp 2-2 as shown by starch-gel electrophoresis, starch block electrophoresis, and by the centrifugation of blood serum. (From Bearn, A. G., and Franklin, E. C.: Some genetical implications of physical studies of human haptoglobins. *Science, 110:*596-597, 1958.)

Finally, there are parts of Africa where Hp^1 has very high frequencies, up to 0.9 and even higher. The haptoglobin polymorphism Hp^1/Hp^2 thus separates Asia from Europe and both from Africa in turn. There is, however, some evidence that the Hp^1 gene increases and the Hp^2 gene decreases approaching the equator from either pole (cf Barnicot *et al.: Nature,* 184:2042, 1959).

The Hp^{2m} gene, mentioned above, is found in approximately 15 per cent of American Negro families. Unknown in Europeans, it is apparent that the Hp^{2m} gene has an African origin, presumably from areas where its frequency is of the order of 0.20 or so (Giblett and Steinberg, 1960).

ISONIAZID INACTIVATION

Isoniazid is a modern drug highly useful in the treatment of tuberculosis, and inactivated at different rates. Rapid inactivators have the liver enzyme that acetylates the drug: slow inactivators are the recessive homozygotes, in turn.

Slow inactivators are less common among Amerinds, Eskimos, Chinese, and Japanese, with allele frequencies from 0.22 (for Eskimos) to 0.40 (for certain American Indians).

Slow inactivators are far more common in Europe, Africa, and the Middle East, with allele frequencies of 0.60 to 0.62 for Italians, Scandanavians, and American Negroes, 0.77 for Greeks, 0.80-0.85 in Sudanese and Middle Eastern Jews, and reaching a maximum of 0.91 in Egyptians. The cradle of European civilization and the cradle of isoniazid acetylating enzyme deficiency appears to be one and the same.

TASTE-BLINDNESS AND RACE

Racial differences in dietary practices have long been viewed with interest, and the suggestion has been made that people who prefer hot, spicy foods differ in taste acuity from those who espouse the cult of culinary blandness. So far, however, conclusive evidence as to racial differences in the classic taste parameters (sweet, sour, salty, and bitter) has not been achieved though there are gene-determined differences in sensitivity.

Nevertheless, there are individual differences in the capacity to taste *phenylthiocarbamide* (PTC) and a large number of related substances, all of which have some antithyroid activity. These differences are apparently controlled by a pair of allelic genes T (for tasting) and t (non-tasting): the genotypes TT and Tt are tasters, and the tt genotype corresponds to the non-taster phenotype. However, there is an hormonal effect as well, as evidenced by the greater proportion of taste-sensitive women. From the work of Fischer and Griffin (1959) taste sensitivity may be explained by the genetically determined level of di-iodo tyrosine in the saliva.

Taste sensitivity varies from population to population. Among American Indians the majority are tasters. In fact some Amerindian populations must approach 1.00 for the taster (T) gene. In Africa and the Middle East the tasters are in the majority. However, in numerous parts of Europe the gene frequency for T is considerably lower and there are up to 43 per cent of non-tasters in India (Fig. 12).

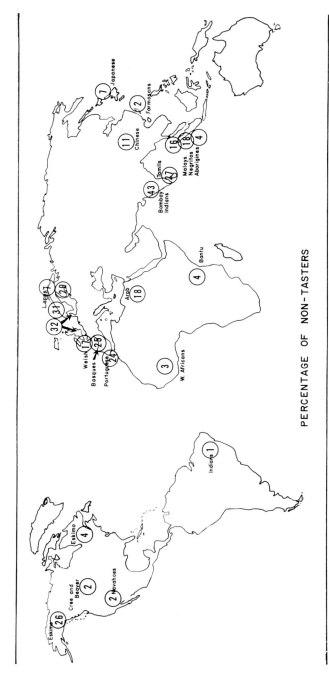

PERCENTAGE OF NON-TASTERS

Fig. 12. Percentage of individuals recorded as "non-tasters" of phenylthiocarbamide and propylthiouracil in various parts of the world, taken from Allison *et al.*, *Human Biol.*, 31:353, 1959, and Salanha and Nacrur, *Am. J. Phys. Anthropol.*, 21:113, 1963. Not only does PTC taste insensitivity appear to relate to the existence of naturally occurring anti-thyroid substances, but there is growing evidence that there is an association between the degree of UTC taste sensitivity and the blinding disease of glaucoma. (For references see *Nutrition Reviews*, 22:298, 1964.)

Boyd has suggested that tasting is adaptive in some areas of the world and inadaptive in others. At the present time the world distribution of PTC-propylthiouracil tasting not only evidences marked race differences but suggests many experiments bearing on PTC taste sensitivity. "Tasters" for example, probably have more food aversions than non-tasters, a quality of limited value in times of scarcity.

RACE DIFFERENCES

Race differences exist throughout the body and into the area of metabolic activity and biochemical functioning. Not only are there race differences in the pigmentation of the skin, eyes, and hair, and in the morphology of the lips, nose, eyelids, and mouth, but there are also differences in the inner organs, in the muscles, and in the patterning of subcutaneous fat. The teeth, hemoglobins and hemoglobin-fixing proteins, taste acuity, drug sensitivity, urinary excretion patterns, and probably sex-hormone activity exhibit measurable differences in averages or proportions from race-population to race-population. To say that "race is only skin deep," a statement notably but inaccurately repeated in many textbooks, is patently naive in the extreme.

Some of the race differences are so marked as to allow little overlapping between geographical races. By way of example, the extreme spiral-tuft form of the head hair is virtually unknown in Europeans. The Rh-negative gene, on the other hand, is rare outside of Europe. For many other traits, it is the frequencies or proportions that are distinctive, as with the haptoglobin types in Europe and Africa. Often, differences are of a small order of magnitude, large enough to attain statistical significance but not impressive enough to use in a taxonomy.

Not infrequently, particular differences *within* geographical races are more marked than those between geographical races. For example, the phenomenon of steatopygia (fat rears) virtually sets off the Bushmen-Hottentot from the rest of Africa, and in body build the Papago are distinct from other Amerindian groups. But a single such difference probably reflecting local selective forces does not alarm the taxonomist, no more than (and for the same reasons) that a run on the bank does not affect the long-term position of a gambling casino.

It is important, however, to emphasize the independence of genes. The fact that genes *P* and *Q* are both common in a given group does not mean that they are inherited together, that they came from the same source. Whereas the *PQ* genotype may be characteristic of a given population, individuals who are *pp* or *qq* are not less "pure" on that account. And since the genes are independent, the existence of the gene *P* in a given population need not be evidence that it came from a *PQ* source. In other words, dark skins are not necessarily of "Negro" origin, nor internal eyefolds inevitably due to "Mongoloid" ancestry. Failure to recognize the independence of genes has led to some rather implausible historical reconstructions in the past.

Races differ in a great many gene-determined respects and a marked difference in the proportion of one set of alleles predicts nothing in respect to the proportions of another set. Moreover, it is not the mere fact of difference that intrigues us today, but rather the source of the difference. The fact that one race has a high frequency of some trait, and there is a low frequency in another race, is mildly interesting as a descriptive fact but no more until we turn our attention to the reasons why.

CERUMEN: STICKY AND DRY

Europeans and Africans know that cerumen (earwax) is sticky, closely resembling the stuff used to shine wood floors and the carnuba wax that once gave the family Ford its artful gloss. But earwax comes in two forms, sticky and dry, and this polymorphism has major racial implications.

The wet-sticky kind of cerumen is the norm in Africans and Europeans, who are close to homozygous for the trait (sticky is dominant over dry.) But about 85 per cent of Japanese have the dry-flaky "rice bran" type of earwax, pointing to a gene frequency of 0.92 or better for the recessive dry cerumen form in them (cf. Matsunaga 1962, and McKusick (1966).

The dry (or Asiatic) form of earwax is the more common type in some groups of American Indians, such as the Navajo (60 to 70 per cent of whom are homozygous for the trait), and in 45 to 55 per cent of other Indians such as the Sioux, the Dakota and others (Petrakis *et al,* 1967). On the other hand, some groups are well under 30 per cent in this respect, either because of admixture or because the original settlers of the Americas were heterozygous having both the dominant (sticky) gene and the recessive (dry) gene, too. But the cerumen polymorphism, like so many others, attests both to the relationships between Amerindians and Asiatics and differences between them as well (cf. Hirschhorn, 1970) and may relate to humidity and temperature (cf. McCullough and Giles, 1970).

Japanese scientists note an association between the sticky form of earwax (which they call "honey earwax" or "cat-ear earwax") and odoriferous axillae. So this earwax polymorphism, which separates East from West, and unites Black and White Americans, may also involve the more specialized glands of the armpit, that are (in adults) under hormonal control.

CHROMOSOMES AND RACE

Normal human beings have 23 pairs of chromosomes, or 46 chromosomes in all, in each somatic cell. Some few individuals, perhaps five in a thousand, have fewer chromosomes (45) or a larger number of chromosomes (47, 48, 49 or more) but most such people are developmentally and mentally abnormal. As with other traits, there are polymorphisms in chromosomal size within normal individuals, and this is especially true for the Y chromosome, one of the short G-group chromosomes.

Measuring Y chromosomes from leucocytes in metaphase and relating them to the size of "standard" chromosomes, there is a marked range of relative lengths, from under 60 per cent to over 150 per cent, by one technique of comparison. Not only is there a wide range of individual values of relative Y-chromosome lengths, but there are group (population) relative differences as well. M. M. Cohen, M. W. Shaw, and J. W. MacCluer (1966) compared relative Y-lengths in individuals of different ancestries as shown in the table, a classic work of fascinating interest.

In other studies, both Jews and Arabs have both been shown to have relatively longer Y chromosomes than East Indians and

Northwestern Europeans. "It is" (as Jerome Lejeune quipped) "the Y chromosome of Abraham."

Ancestral Group	Index Y_F	Y_2
Japanese	1.00	0.33
Jews	0.94	0.29
American Negroes	0.92	0.30
East Indians	0.88	0.29
Northwest European	0.86	0.27

Since no Y-linked genes have definitely been identified, and since the Y chromosome is not necessary for life, the practical significance of relative Y-lengths is at present unclear. The greater Y-length in Japanese is (apparently) associated with an even greater relative variability, suggesting a bimodal distribution. So far the only likely explanation is that smaller Y chromosomes are more likely to become lost. Hereditary differences in Y-chromosome length have been known since 1962. The meaning of group differences in relative Y-lengths is now open for investigation.

SUMMARY

Racial differences are known to exist in almost every area of anatomy where comparative data have been accumulated, and there is growing evidence for race differences in biochemical functioning and in the constituents of cells and tissues.

In a minority of examples, there may be little overlapping between geographical races. Much more frequently, differences are merely matters of proportion, the incidence of different traits, or the frequencies of the allelic genes that determine them. Not infrequently a given gene-determined trait varies more extensively among local races in the same geographical race than between geographical races.

The independence of the genes that make for similarities and differences must be clearly understood. Thus two races may be markedly different with respect to one allelic pair of genes and not at all different with respect to another. Taken alone, therefore, a particular set of differences (or similarities) says nothing as to communality or divergence origin or descent.

SUGGESTED READINGS

Barnicot, N. A., and Wolffson, D.: Daily urinary 17-ketosteroid output of African Negroes. *The Lancet, 262:*893-898, 1952.

Blumberg, B. S., and Gartler, S. M.: The urinary excretion of β-aminoisobutyric acid in Pacific populations. *Human Biol., 33:*355-362, 1961.

Chagula, W. K.: The age at eruption of third permanent molars in male East Africans. *Am. J. Phys. Anthropol.,* N.S. 18:77-82, 1960.

Cockshott, P.: Carpal fusions. *Am J. Roent., 89:*1260-1271, 1963.

Cohen, M. M., Shaw, M. W., and MacCluer, J. W.: Racial differences in the length of the human Y chromosome. *Cytogenetics, 5:*34-52, 1966.

Fisher, R., and Griffin, F. On factors involved in the mechanism of "taste-blindness." *Experientia, 15:*447-451, 1959.

Garn, S. M.: *The Earlier Gain and the Later Loss of Cortical Bone: In Nutritional Perspective.* Springfield, Thomas, 1970.

Garn, S. M.: Types and distribution of the hair in man. In Hamilton, J. B. (Ed.) : The Growth, Replacement and Types of Hair, *Annals of the N. Y. Academy of Sciences, 53:*498-507, 1951.

Garn, S .M., Fels, S. L., and Israel, H.: Brachymesophalangia of digit five in ten populations. *Am. J. Phys. Anthropol., 27:*205-210, 1967.

Garn, S. M., Lewis, A. B., and Walenga, A. J.: Crown-size profile pattern comparisons of 14 human population. *Archs. Oral Biol., 13:*1235-1242, 1968.

Garn, S. M., and Moorrees, C. F. A.: Body-build and tooth emergence in Aleutian Aleut children. *Child Development, 22:*262-270, 1951.

Garn, S. M., Pao, E. M., and Rihl, M. E.: Compact bone in Chinese and Japanese. *Science, 143:*1438-1439, 1964.

Gartler, S. M., Firschein, I. L., and Kraus, B. S.: An investigation into the genetics and arcial variation of BAIB excretion. *Am. J. Human Genet., 9:*200-207, 1957.

Gartler, S. M., Firschein, I. L., and Gidaspow, T.: Some genetical and anthropological considerations of urinary β-aminoisobutyric acid excretion. *Acta Genetica, 6:*435-466, 1956/7.

Hamilton, J. B.: Patterned loss of hair in man, types and incidence. In Hamilton, J. B. (Ed.) : The Growth, Replacement and Types of Hair. *Annals of the N. Y. Academy of Sciences, 53:*708-728, 1951.

Hertzog, K. P., Garn, S. M., and Church, S. F.: Cone-shaped epiphyses in the hand. *Inv Radiol., 3:*433-441, 1968.

Hirschhorn, H. H.: Cerumen types and PTC-tasting in Seminole Indians of Florida. *Am. J. Phys. Anthropol., 33:*107-108, 1970.

Hoyme, L. E.: Genetics, physiology and phenylthiocarbamide. *J. Hered., 46:*167-175, 1955.

Lasker, G. W.: Genetic analysis of racial traits of the teeth, *Cold Spring Harbor Symposia on Quantitative Biology, 15:*191-203, Cold Spring Harbor, The Biological Laboratory, 1950.

Lasker, G. W., Mast, J., and Tashian, R.: β-aminoisobutyric acid (BAIB) excretion in urine of residents of eight communities in the States of Michoacan and Oaxaca, Mexico, *Am. J. Phys. Anthropol., 30:*133-136, 1969.

Lee, M. M. C., and Lasker, G. W.: The sun-tanning potential of human skin, *Human Biol., 31:*252-260, 1959.

Makela, O., Erikson, A. W., and Lehtovaara, B.: On the inheritance of the haptoglobin serum groups. *Acta Genetica et Statistica Medica, 9:*149-166, 1959.

Martin, R., and Saller, K.: *Lehrbuch der Anthropologie,* Stuttgart, Gustav Fischer, 1959.

Matsunaga, E.: The dimorphism in human normal cerumen. *Ann. Hum. Genet., 25:*273-286, 1962.

McCullough, J. M., and Giles, E.: Human cerumen types in Mexico and New Guinea: A humidity-related polymorphism in "Mongoloid" peoples. *Nature, 226:*460-462, 1970.

McKusick, V. A.: *Mendelian Inheritance in Man.* Baltimore, Johns Hopkins Press, 1966.

Moorrees, C. F. A.: *The Aleut Dentition,* Cambridge, Harvard University Press, 1957.

Moorrees, C. F. A.: Torus mandibularis: its occurrence in Aleut children and its genetic determinants. *Am. J. Phys. Anthropol.,* N.S. *10:*319-330, 1952.

O'Rahilly, R.: Developmental deviations in the carpus and the tarsus. *Clin. Ortho., 10:*9-18, 1957.

Petrakis, N. L., Molohon, K. T., and Tepper, D. J.: Cerumen in American Indians: genetic implications of sticky and dry types. *Science, 158:*1192-1193, 1967.

Schultz, A. H.: Fetal growth of man and other primates. *Quart. Rev. Biol., 1:*465-521, 1926.

Steggerda, M., and Hill, T. C.: Eruption time of teeth among Whites, Negroes and Indians, *Am. J. Orthodont. and Oral Surg., 28:*361-370, 1942.

Steinberg, A. G., and Matsumoto, H.: Studies on the Gm, Inv. Hp and Tf serum factors of Japanese populations and families. *Human Biol. 36:*77-85, 1964.

Sutton, H. E., and Clark, P. G.: A biochemical study of Chinese and Caucasoids. *Am. J. Phys. Anthropol.,* N.S. *13:*53-66, 1955.

Trotter, M., Broman, G. E., and Peterson, R. R.: Density of cervical vertebrae and comparison with densities of other bones. *Am. J. Phys. Anthropol.,* N.S. *17:*19-25, 1959.

IV

BLOOD GROUPS AND RACE

For MANY centuries the possibility of transfusing blood has appealed to surgeons. Great numbers of men died from loss of blood following accidents or battle. Patients expired during and following operations, patients who could have been saved by blood transfusion. But until 1900 transfusions were impractical: too often they ended in shock and death. Somehow, blood just didn't mix.

Then, about seventy years ago, Landsteiner discovered the existence of four different blood types which he named types A, B, AB, and O. By determining the blood "type" of the patient, and transfusing compatible blood, blood transfusions became a fortunate practicality. And, as a result of the extensive work on blood-typing, during and since World War I, a tremendous amount has been learned about blood types and their relation to local and geographical races.

THE ABO SYSTEM

The original four types of Landsteiner are called the ABO system. These blood types are simply inherited with both A and B dominant over O. Genetically, type O blood is OO, while the phenotypes A and B may be either AA or OA, and BB or OB respectively.

Blood Type	Possible Genotypes
A	AA, OA
B	BB, OB
AB	AB
O	OO

Of the three blood types (or factors) in the ABO system, O is the most common the world over. Among some American Indian groups, over 90 per cent of the people are of blood group

O, with gene frequencies for O as high as 0.99. In much of Europe, the incidence of O is from 35% to 40%, and the frequency of the gene r is between 0.6 and 0.7. Among Chinese, Japanese, and Asiatic Indians and in many African populations, O may be as low as 30% with a gene frequency of as little as 0.5. However, even within a particular geographical race there are marked differences in the incidence of O. By way of example, O has been reported in 97 per cent of Utes, but in only 23 per cent of Blackfoot Indians. In Europe there is an increasing incidence of blood type O from south to north, a trend that is repeated even within the British Isles.

Blood group A, the next most frequent blood type the world around, similarly evidences its own pattern of distribution. It is rare (under 5%) in some Amerindian populations, yet extremely common (over 75%) in others; both are world extremes and point to the wide divergences possible between local races. By way of comparison, the phenotype frequency of A is about 45% in England (with a gene frequency of 0.25) and the same among Americans of Northwest European descent.

Blood group B, the least common of the three types in the ABO system, has the most interesting world distribution. It is completely absent in most North and South American Indians, rarely over 2% in others, and this may be due to admixture. Blood group B is less common than A in Europe, with a phenotype frequency of 9% to 25%, averaging about 15%. However, B, which increases in frequency to 22% in Ukrainians and 25% in Egyptians, reaches maxima of 35% to 37% in China, Java, Bengal, and the Siberian north. B is an Asiatic and African blood type much more than it is European, and it is not all Amerindian.

Comparing Sumatra, Java, and the Philippines with Polynesians, there is a great divergence in AOB blood groups. The Asiatic-Malaysian areas are high in B, whereas Polynesia is low in B (under 3%). Clearly Polynesians cannot be derived from any recent mixture with Malaysian people. In similar fashion, the low to zero incidence of blood group B in aboriginal America precludes major recent contact with Asiatic Mongoloids whose frequency of B ranges from 20% to 40% in different populations.

However, blood type A is divisible into two subtypes, A_1 and A_2; of the two A_1 is far more common than A_2. The incidence of A_2 varies from zero (in Amerindians and Australians) to 10% to 15% in much of Europe. American Indians agree with Asiatic Mongoloids in the virtual absence of A_2, as is true of Polynesia and Australia as well. In fact, A_2 is practically limited to Europe and Africa.

Broadly, the ABO blood system can be summarized by noting (1) the near absence of B and absence of A_2 in the Americas, (2) the low to moderate frequencies of B and increasing frequency of A_2 in Europe, and (3) the high incidence of B and relative rarity of A_2 in Asia. But the Australian aborigines seem practically Amerindian, as do the Polynesians in their low incidence of B and absence of A_2. The ABO system, taken alone, would suggest a separate origin for them, whereas it groups Asia, India, and Africa.

THE MNS-U SYSTEM

Next to the classic ABO system is the MNS-U system, involving a locus on the third or fourth chromosome, and with population differences exceeding those for A, B, and O. It is in M and N that Australian aborigines and American Indians are most different and exclude Pacific contacts in South America.

As with A and B, M and N are inherited without dominance, A person may be M, N, or MN, corresponding to the genotypes MM, NN, and MN. For much of the world, the frequencies of M and N are about equal, and rarely is either M or N entirely missing. Thus, in England the gene frequencies for M and N are close to 0.53 and 0.47 and in Japan they approximate 0.56 and 0.44 respectively.

But M is peculiarly high among the American Indians, and in many Amerindian tribes there is little or no N. (Low values for N have also been reported for the Near East.) In contrast to the situation in America, Australia is the virtual homeland of N; and M, that is MM, individuals are entirely absent in some aboriginal hordes. Throughout the Pacific, in Papua, Fiji, and Hawaii blood type N is similarly predominant over M. Whereas these peoples of the Pacific are similar to Amerindians in the low incidence of B and of the subtype A_2, the high N frequencies of Pacific people set them off completely and preclude recent major contact with America, as their absence of B does with Asia.

Since the extremes of M and N are found in populations formerly explained on the basis of "admixture," it is notable that no combination of Asiatics could yield the low N values common in America, and no Caucasoid-Negroid combinations could yield the nearly M-free people of Australia. Either the "original" three races never existed, or subsequent evolution has so altered their genetic makeup in particular localities as to make proof of the three-race hypothesis quite impossible.

Still, two additions to the M-N system must be made. One involves the rare gene S, discovered in 1947, which involves a mutation alternately from M or from N. A person may be MS, MNS or NS. The S gene, discovered in England, (where it is quite common) has since been shown to be absent in Australian aborigines, but present in natives of New Guinea. Tentatively, therefore, one may suggest either closer affinities between Papuans and Europeans, or an absence of this between the Australian and European geographical race. Perhaps MS and NS might be called M_2 and N_2, in which case we could say that both M_2 and N_2 are fairly common in Europe, but absent among the aboriginal Australians.

A second addition to the MNS system involves the gene U, sometimes written as S^u. Among Europeans everyone is U-positive. In Negroes, or more specifically the American Colored, about 1% are U-negative as shown below. This polymorphism leads to complications, both in transfusions and in childbirth. Transfusing U-positive blood into a U-negative Negro can be dangerous.

U-NEGATIVE PHENOTYPE AND GENE FREQUENCIES

	No.	U+	U—	Gene Frequency
Milwaukee "Caucasians"	10,000	10,000	0	0.00
Milwaukee Negroes	1,429	1,425	4	0.05
New York Negroes	989	977	12	0.11

From Greenwalt, Sasaki, Sanger, and Race (1956), and Sampson *et al.* (1959.

While segregated blood stores would not be the answer (most Negroes are U-postitive as are nearly all Europeans) the necessity to consider race in planning transfusions becomes all the more apparent. Further divergences in Negro blood groups will be mentioned later in this chapter.

RHESUS AND RACE

By now, most educated individuals have heard about the *Rhesus factor* and Rh incompatibility. They know that, especially in later pregnancies, a rhesus-positive fetus can be damaged by antibodies produced by the Rh-negative mother.

Actually, there is long series of rhesus genes, R_1, R_2, R_0, r', r, variously written as R', R'', etc. Practically, R_1, R_2, r', and others are dominant over the rhesus-negative gene, which will therefore be written as r;* the rhesus-negative individual is a homozygous rr.

Among Europeans in whom the rhesus-negative gene was first discovered, the proportion of Rh-negative individuals ranges from about 12% through an average of approximately 15% in England and the United States, to nearly 30% in Basques.

Elsewhere in the world, rhesus-negative blood is rare, uncommon, or even totally absent. A long series of American Indians and many series of Papuans or Australian aborigines can be compiled with few or no rhesus-negative individuals. Rhesus-negative blood is also absent in Polynesia and uncommon in China, Japan, and the Philippines, though the incidence begins to rise in India, Pakistan, and Afghanistan.

Among American Negroes the type rr is about half as common as in northwest Europeans, leading expectably to its relative rarity in the sections of Africa whence their African gene originated. However, the type R_0, which rarely exceeds 2% in Europe, achieves maxima of more than 40% in the American Colored, and over 70% in Africa. It is for this reason that the R_0 gene in Melanesia is of interest.

---

*The notation for the Rh alleles used here is primarily that of Alexander Weiner though it does not follow his more recent revisions. Abroad there is a totally different notation developed by R. A. Fisher, which involves different assumptions about the mode of inheritance.

The present distribution of the "rhesus" blood types, the high frequency of the gene r in Europe and especially among the Basques, the rarity of r in Asia, Australia, Polynesia, and aboriginal America, and the concentration of R_0 in Africa, cannot be explained in any simple way. One is loath to accept Boyd's "early" Europeans, who presumably contributed vast numbers of the rhesus-negative genes in Europe and were then absorbed by latecomers. Even if there had been such a population, we are still faced with the continued survival of this disadvantageous gene, the more so under primitive conditions. And we wonder what value R_0 has in Africa.

DUFFY, AN AUSTRALASIAN GENE

In 1950, a new blood-group factor, unrelated to the ABO, MN and Rh systems, was found in the blood of a Mr. Duffy, and the new system that eventuated from this chance event was named after him. The Duffy factor soon proved important in transfusions, as a cause of transfusion reactions.

Briefly, there is the Duffy-positive gene (Fy^a) and the Duffy-negative allelomorph (Fy^b). A person may be Fy^aFy^a, Fy^bFy^b, or Fy^aFy^b. However, since, Fy^a is dominant over Fy^b, only two phenotypes are identifiable. Therefore, phenotype frequencies of Fy^b are used in computing the gene frequencies for Fy^b and Fy^a respectively.

In England 65 per cent of subjects proved to be Duffy-positive, corresponding to a gene frequency of 0.40. Far higher gene frequencies for Fy^a have appeared in Pakistan, India, and among New York Chinese, and Australians. Far lower gene frequencies were observed in American Colored individuals (see table). In fact, the rarity of Duffy-positive individuals in Africa and the relatively high frequency of the dominant gene in people of English ancestry, makes the Duffy system the most sensitive measure of European admixture in the American Colored breeding population. Reed has used this principle to measure admixture as will be discussed in Chapter IX.

Obviously, the home of the Duffy-positive gene is in the Pacific and Eastern Asia with decreasing frequencies both southward

FREQUENCIES OF THE DUFFY-POSITIVE
(Fy^a) GENE

Group Studied	Gene Frequency Fy^a
Cape York Australians	1.00
Koreans	0.99
Chinese	0.91
Japanese	0.86
East Indians	0.73
American Indians	0.50-1.00
English donors	0.41
Minnesota Whites	0.40
American Colored	0.14

From Matson and Swanson (1959), Simmons *et al.* (1958), and Race and Sanger (1954).

into the Americas and westward into Europe and then Africa where the Fy^a gene is virtually absent. The distribution of Fy^a, if taken seriously by proponents of a simple three-race theory, would provide better evidence that the Europeans are of mixed Polynesian-Negro origin (since they are intermediate in Fy^a frequencies) than for any tri-hybrid origin for the Polynesian peoples!

DIEGO, A MOSTLY "ASIATIC" BLOOD GROUP

The Diego blood group system, one of the most recently discovered, involves a pair of genes Di^a and Di^b, and the two phenotypes, Diego "positive" and Diego negative. Though Diego-positive individuals are nowhere in the majority, the Di^a gene clearly separates Australia and the Pacific from Asia and the Americas (Fig. 13).

In two series of Australians, one in the north nearest New Guinea, and one in Central Australia, no Diego-positive individuals were found. Similarly the Diego antigen appears to be absent in the eastern Polynesians. On the other hand, Diego-positive individuals have been reported in 25 per cent of Peruvian Indians and 10 per cent of Penobscot Indians, but rarely among Alaskan (Tlingit) Indians and Alaskan Eskimos. Several studies confirm the virtual absence of Di^a in Alaska and the relatively high frequencies in Central America.

Despite the absence of the dominant Di^a gene in Alaska, Diego-positive individuals are frequently found among Chinese,

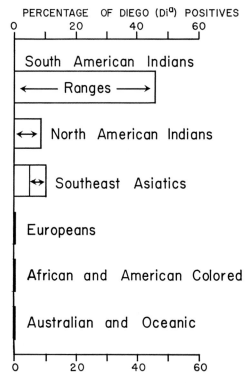

Fig. 13. Percentage of Diego-"positive" individuals in different populations. The genotype Di^a or Di^{a+} is largely restricted to Amerindians and Asiatics. (Adapted from Layrisse, M., Wilbert, J., and Arends, T.: Frequency of blood group antigens in the descendants of Guayqueri Indians, *Am. J. Phys. Anthropol., N. S. 16*:307-318, 1958).

Japanese, and Koreans. This suggests, quite reasonably, an Asiatic source of Diego in the Americas. However the extremely variable phenotypic frequencies in Central and North America, ranging from 0% to over 20% and the absence of Diego nearest the Asiatic mainland can be explained only in terms of local selection.

Rarely, Di^a may be found in individuals of European origin, as Simmons, Albrea, Morgan, and Smith (1968) point out, but it is then a one-in-a-million affair.

SUMMARY OF PRINCIPAL BLOOD GROUP SYSTEMS

Blood Group System	Description of Phenotype Frequencies
ABO (including A_1 & A_2)	O most common group, with over 50% of individuals in most populations of this type. B nearly absent in aboriginal America and Australia, progressively more common in Europe (15%), Africa, India and Asia (up to 40%). A_2 practically limited to Europe. A_2 does not exist in aboriginal Australia or New Guinea.[††]
MNS-U (or S^u)	American Indians almost exclusively M; N most common in Australia and the Pacific. MS and NS absent in Australia. U-negative rare, apparently limited to Africa.[*]
Rh (R_1 R_2 R_0 r' r etc.)	Rh-negative individuals *(rr)* rare or absent in most of the world, but approximately 15% in Europeans. Of the Rh-positive alleles (R_1, R_2 etc.) the R_0 form is primarily found in Africa (up to 70%). R_0 variants exist in New Guinea.[††]
Duffy (Fy^a Fy^b Fy)	Most Australians and Polynesians[§] and 90% to 99% of Asiatics Duffy-positive (Fy^a), 90% in India, 85% to 90% of most American Indian,[**] 65% in England and America, 27% in American Negroes. Fy^a very low in Africa but the gene Fy extremely common (>80%).[†] New Guinea and Africa are polar extremes.[††]
Diego (Di^a Di^b)	Diego-positive (Di^a) individuals limited to Amerindians (2% to 20%), and Asiatics.[*] Di^a absent in Europe and Africa, Australia, Micronesia and Polynesia,[§] and in Eskimos.[*] Extremely rare in Europeans (see Simmons, Albrey *et al.*, 1968.
Kidd (Jk^a Jk^b)	Kidd-positive (Jk^a) most common in West Africa and American Colored (>90%), North American Indians (70% to 90%), Europeans (approximately 70%), and least common in Chinese (50% to 55%).[†**]

Special References: [*]Greenwalt *et al.* (1956), [†]Race and Sanger (1954), [§]Simmons, Graydon, and Gajdusek (1958), [**]Simmons *et al.* (1967/1968), [††]Matson and Swanson (1959).[*]

BLOOD GROUPS AND NATURAL SELECTION

As a result of numerous investigations involving millions of people, it is extremely clear that the blood groups are subject to natural selection. Population differences in blood group frequencies may therefore be viewed as the product of competing lines of selection, the balancing of selective advantages and disadvantages associated with each serological type.

Classic Rh incompatibility, the loss of an Rh heterozygous

---

[*]Levine has shown a protective effect of certain ABO genotypes against Rh incompatibility. See *Human Biol.*, *30*:14-28, 1958.

infant[†] due to antibody formation in a Rh-negative mother, is the best known example of selection against a blood type. The long-term effect of such incompatibility would be to eliminate the Rh⁻ gene *(r)* from the population, and this may explain the rarity or absence of the Rh-negative gene in much of the world. At the same time we need some explanation for the continuance of this gene in Europe, especially among the Basques.

Less well known, but equally important, is maternal-fetal incompatibility in the ABO system. Since the net effect would be to eliminate types A and B differentially in comparison to O, this may provide an explanation for the numerical predominance of O the world around. Moreover, now that transfusion reactions have been discovered for a variety of other blood group factors, including the rare U in the MNS-U system, it is obvious that the increasing use of blood transfusions is serving to eliminate some proportion of the less common genes in each population.

ABO incompatibilities are also responsible for infertility with natural selection operating against particular genotypes prior to conception according to Heglar.* Alternatively it is possible that in heterozygotic males more sperm of a particular genotype is produced, making for differential selection in respect to the classic ABO blood types.

Associations between ABO types and chronic illnesses have been demonstrated, among them associations between type O and ulcers, and type A and gastric cancer, in the U.S.A., in Europe, and in Japan. O may be associated with increased adult bone loss, but with fewer abnormalities of the clotting mechanisms in women taking oral contraceptives.

In view of the fact that the blood groups are subject to selection the use of serological data in historical reconstructions is obviously limited. It would be unwise to guess as to the frequency of B in Asia ten thousand years ago, or even the frequency of the Rh-negative gene among "early" Europeans. However,

---

[†]Recent advances in neonatal care greatly minimize the hazards of maternal-fetal incompatibility and may bring about a new genetic balance in the Rh series.

*Matsunaga and Hirazumi: *Science, 135:*432, 1962; Heglar, *Am. J. Phys. Anthropol., 19:*98, Matsunaga: *J. Med. Educ., 34:*405-13, 1959.

since all lines of selection now known would tend toward population homozygosity, special attention should be given to situations where, as with the Duffy factor in Europe, maximum number of heterozygotes exist. There may well be a real adaptive advantage to being MN, Fy^aFy^b, and possibly AB. In fact, there are more MN children from MN x MN marriages than one might expect even if technical errors are to some extent involved (Morton *et al.*, 1959).

ASSOCIATIONS BETWEEN BLOOD GROUPS AND DISEASE

Except for erythroblastosis fetalis, involving ABO and Rh incompatibilities, the numerous associations between blood groups and disease have been statistical and inferential rather than obvious and direct. Despite the large number of associations, it is not certain that in any single disease situation the disorder is a product of the antigen. In a recent discussion in the *American Journal of Human Genetics* these points have been made. Vogel (*22*:464-475, 1970) writes:

> In conclusion, associations between ABO blood groups and disease have been established beyond any reasonable doubt. They seem to influence fitness in higher age groups under modern living conditions. Under primitive conditions, a relationship of the ABO blood groups with resistance to infectious diseases, and hence an influence on natural selection, is very likely. However, the physiological basis of the associations is not yet clearly understood. The hypotheses available to date have not found general acceptance. In view of the ubiquitous occurrence of blood group determinants and their obvious importance for human health, this problem provides a challenge for experimental immunologists.

Wiener, however, long a skeptic of blood group disease association, summarizes his stand as follows (*22*:476-483, 1970) :

> Thus, it is revealing that while the discovery of the role of maternofetal blood group incompatibility in the pathogenesis of erythroblastosis fetalis opened up a new field of medical science—immunohematology—the studies on association of blood groups and other diseases are at exactly the same point today as fifty years ago. While routine Rh testing is an essential part of prenatal care, no one has yet suggested the use of blood grouping tests in the differential diagnosis of duodenal ulcer, pernicious anemia, carcinoma of the lungs, or the like, despite the published claims of associations.

BLOOD GROUPS AND HUMAN TAXONOMY

The blood groups are simply inherited and therefore qualify as ideal traits for use in racial comparisons. Blood group determinations can be made with relatively high reliability except for the less common antigens (Osborne, 1958), and this commends them for general use. Besides, blood group determinations are made by the millions every year in the course of blood donating and transfusions, thus providing a wealth of free information on blood groups in different races.

All of these advantages were clearly recognized over forty years ago, and the idea of a serological taxonomy was advanced. After all, blood groups are genetical, accurate, stable, and susceptible to statistical analyses. A serological taxonomy made at least as much sense, and in fact more, than a classification based on hair form or skin color.

But the first serological taxonomies were hardly reasonable. Using the ABO system, Asia, India, and Africa ended up in one pile (based on the frequency of B), and aboriginal America and Australia in a second sorting (based on an absence of B). Totally unrelated populations were characterized by similarities in ABO frequencies and contiguous groups compared serologically were practically in separate planets.

The situation improved somewhat with the discovery of the subtypes of A, which belatedly confirmed Amerindian-Asiatic similarities and no longer made Europe an apparent Asiatic-Australoid mixture. M-N data further appeared reasonable, geographically as well as genetically. The most unusual distributions of M and N were geographically most isolated from Europe, Asia, and Africa.

With the discovery of the Rhesus system of alleles, serological and geographical taxonomies became more nearly reconciled. Africa appeared clearly separable from Asia (despite high frequencies of B) and Europe from both. Even so, considerable juggling was necessary to make serological taxonomies coincide with natural populations. What had happened to the serologists was exactly what had happened to morphologists. Using the conventional systems of differences they had confused their criteria (here the blood groups) with the races they were trying to describe. By near-sightedly working with the gene frequencies and ratios, they had come up with an artificial classification, a system of blood groups rather than a classification based on natural populations. To the extent that serological classifications worked, they were attempts to describe natural populations (as Boyd has done in his Boston University Lecture).* When the classifications were based on serological criteria, rather than the populations, the results were understandably bizarre.

Actually, the major contribution of the blood groups is not the establishment of a taxonomy, but to the more adequate comparison of related race-populations, their similarities and differences. By way of example, the virtual absence of B in Australia (except in the Cape York area) and the absence of S (that is MS and NS) confirms the separation of Australian and Papuan peoples. At the same time, the absence of Diego and the high frequencies of N align the Australians with other peoples of the Pacific. Similarly, the similarities between Amerindians and Asiatics in the Duffy factor and in Diego are balanced by the differences (in blood group B and possibly in the Kidd blood group).

Particularly for populations formed by recent admixture, the blood groups afford precise quantification. Using the Rh-negative gene (r), the R_0 gene, the incidence of the U-negative trait, Duffy (that is Fy^a), and the Kidd-positive trait, very exact estimates of the degree of intermixture can be obtained for the American Colored and Cape Colored populations, and for various tri-racial hybrids. Similarly, extensive incorporation of Amerindian genes into the American Colored population can be ruled out by serological data. With such information on hand, deviations from expected proportions of various gene-determined traits, such as the abnormal haemoglobins, may then be attributed to natural selection.

---

*Both in his earlier book and in his Boston University Lecture, Boyd's system of "races" properly involved serological descriptions of natural populations rather than serological races based on blood-group frequencies alone. For a discussion on "artificial" keys to taxonomy see Chapter XI.

But the blood groups themselves are subject to selection. Unquestionably, there has been selection against the rhesus-negative gene, and against both A and B in favor of O, at least in Europeans. For these reasons, present gene frequencies do not provide a perfect indication of what they were in the past, and guessing as to proportions of groups entering into ancient admixture becomes a most hazardous activity. Valuable as they are in the study of contemporary populations, the blood groups are of limited value in solving ancient ties between races, but so are the conventional morphological traits.

SUMMARY

The blood groups discovered since 1900 have added tremendously to the scientific study of race. No comparisons can now be made without them. All reconstructions and searches for origins must use the ABO, MNS, Rh, Kell, Kidd, Duffy, Diego, and Lutheran blood group systems. As with purely morphological traits, early "serological races" did not advance human taxonomy, but with an increasing number of loci it is increasingly useful to employ the blood groups, realizing that selection and drift and historic accidents of sampling do operate on the blood groups as with other, but polygenic and environmentally plastic, taxonomic criteria.

SUGGESTED READINGS

*Allison, A. C.: Aspects of polymorphism in man. *Cold Spring Harbor Symposia on Quantitative Biology, 20:*239-255, Cold Spring Harbor, The Biological Laboratory, 1955.

Boyd, W. C.: *Genetics and the Races of Man.* Boston, Little, Brown and Company, 1950.

*Boyd, W. C.: *Genetics and the Races of Man.* Boston University Lecture, Boston University Press, 1958.

*Garn, S. M.: Race and evolution. *Am. Anthropol., 59:*218-224, 1957. *Readings on Race,* pp. 187-189, 1960.

Greenwalt, T. J., Sasaki, T., Sanger, R., and Race, R. R.: S^u an allele of S and s. *Bibliotheca Haemotologica, 7:*104-106, 1956.

---

*Reprinted in *Readings on Race.*

Matson, G. A., and Swanson, J.: Distribution of hereditary blood antigens among the Maya and non-Maya Indians in Mexico and Guatemala. *Am. J. Phys. Anthropol., N.S. 17:*49-74, 1959.

Matsunaga, E.: Selection in ABO polymorphism in Japanese populations. *J. Med. Educ., 34:*405-13, 1959.

Morton, N. E., and Chung, C. S.: Are the MN blood groups maintained by selection? *Am J. Human Genetics, 11:*237-51, 1959.

Mourant, A. E.: *The Distribution of Blood Groups in Animals and Humans.* Springfield, Thomas, 1956.

Osborne, R. H.: Serology in physical anthropology. Technical problems as revealed by repeated blood determinations in twins. *Am. J. Phys. Anthropol.,* N.S. *16:*187-195, 1958.

Race, R. R., and Sanger, R.: *Blood Groups in Man.* Springfield, Thomas, 1954.

Reed, T. E.: Caucasian genes in American Negroes. *Science, 165:*762-768, 1969.

Sampson, C. C., Thomas, C., and Griffin, S.: Isosensitization to the U factor. *J. Am. Med. Assn., 171:*1203-1204, 1959.

Simmons, R. T.: The Diego (Di^a) blood group: tests in some Pacific peoples. *Nature, 179:*970-971, 1957.

Simmons, R. T., Albrey, J. A., Morgan, J. A. G., and Smith, A. L.: The Diego blood group found in Caucasians. *Med. J. Austral., 1:* 406-407, 1968.

Simmons, R. T., Gajdusek, D. C., and Nicholson, M. R.: Blood group genetic variations in inhabitants of West New Guinea. *Am. J. Phys. Anthropol., 27:*277-298, 1967.

Simmons, R. T., Graydon, J. J., Curtain, C. C., and Baumgarten, A.: Blood group studies in Lalagam and Mt. Hagen (Lepers) New Guinea. *Arch. and Phys. Anthropol Oceania, 3:*49-54, 1968.

Simmons, R. T., Gradon, J. J., and Gajdusek, D. C.: A blood group genetical survey in Australian aboriginal children of the Cape York Peninsula. *Am. J. Phys. Anthropol.,* N.S. *16:*59-77, 1958.

V

NATURAL SELECTION AND RACE

In the *Origin of Species,* an epochal book published one hundred years ago, Charles Darwin described the principal mechanism of evolutionary change. Pointing out the inherent variability of all living species and their tendency to depart infinitely from a central type, Darwin saw in natural selection the directive force behind each species and smaller taxonomic units as well.

Natural selection provides a mechanism for change within species and especially within races. With natural selection in operation each race undergoes continual change. Ultimately, the descendants scarcely resemble their ancestors, phenotypically and genotypically as well. Though the many races of mankind derive from a common source, they have come to differ widely, both among themselves, and from their first *sapiens* progenitor.

Natural selection involves no mystery, no mirrors, no "will to change" and no *elan vital.* All of the environmental forces we see about us are potential selective agents, bringing about, through genetic adaptation, differentiation between races. Food is a selective agent, by its abundance favoring fertility and by its scarcity favoring reduced size and diminished growth. Diseases are powerful selective agents, favoring in each generation those with superior immunochemical properties. The natural world and the man-made world are full of forces that shape races and make one race ultimately different from another.

Thus, when we view a race, long-established in a particular climatic zone, habituated to specific foods and levels of caloric intake, and subjected to local diseases, our first inclination is to explore the immediate environment for selective factors responsible for local differentiation. Or, having caught sight of some unusual difference, we may choose to investigate it alone and to determine what adaptive advantage its presence or absence may convey.

However, since local environments are multitudinous (and for the most part ill-explored), it becomes quite a task to assess the race-making potentiality of a bog here and a swamp there. Individual human differences, numbering in the thousands, present a comparably formidable task to analyze. How do we measure the evolutionary significance of the inner or "Mongolian" eyefold, the reasons for a given gene frequency among the Tlingit, or the reasons for peculiar Duffy and Diego frequencies among the Lacandons?

Here the broad-gauge view comes into its own. Instead of trying to match each racial difference to its corresponding selective advantage, we often search for broad generalizations involving variables of climate or major somatic differences. We look for characteristics particularly associated with extreme heat or cold. We look for climatic variables differentially associated with body build or skin pigmentation. We watch for diseases that may explain the distribution of the abnormal haemoglobins. In short, and detective-wise, we seek for clues that may explain particular directions of racial differentiation, as well as the process of race-making in general.

ENVIRONMENTAL DIFFERENCES

One major environmental difference is temperature, and with it the intensity of solar radiation. World extremes run above 130° F. *in the shade,* to minus 60 and below, a range of 190°F. Usually, the extremes are found in very different regions, but in the desert soil-temperatures may drop from 125°F. at midday, to below freezing the very same night. The same man may come near to blistering his feet at noon and frosting his toes in sleep. This is true in the Kalahari, in the deserts of Australia, and in the deserts of the American southwest.

Solar radiation, contributing to the radiant heat load, varies by a factor of nearly 10,000. An exposure meter may go off-scale in the desert and barely yield a reading in the Arctic night-day. It is true that houses, umbrellas, central heating, and air-conditioned rooms mitigate the extremes for many of us now, but this is not true for all, and such protection against nature is relatively recent in man's million-year existence. When we read of death by sunstroke or by cold, we may well realize how much more stringent climatic selection was a hundred and a thousand years ago, and what a large proportion of the population faced climatic extremes with relatively little environmental protection.

We in America and Western Europe have unlimited access to food. With no additional cost we could become circus fat-men, ingesting a daily 6,000 calories instead of our national averages of 2,000 to 3,000 calories a day. Overnutrition is clearly a major cause of death with us: as a population we are adapting to a food surfeit. But in many parts of the world, 1,500 calories a day (a weight-reducing value for us) is a feast, and 800 calories per day is unfortunately "normal" for many. Our breakfast of bacon and eggs, buttered toast, and coffee with cream provides as much meat as many people get in a week and is comparable in fat to several days' food for them. An American adult drinks more milk in a few days than most African and Asiatic toddlers see in a year. As with temperature, extremes in food intake are great. Death by starvation is in fact far more common than death by heat or cold.

Besides temperature and food, there are numerous infectious diseases that slaughter people by the billions. In Lincoln's time, Americans died in great numbers of cholera, typhus, malaria, diphtheria, scarlet fever, pneumonia, tuberculosis, and dysentery. Quite recently, Eskimos succumbed to measles and mumps and whooping cough. In other parts of the world malaria, elephantiasis and yaws, amoebic dysentery, and snail-carried Bilharzia are common causes of death. Little wonder that in some primitive areas today scarcely one infant in three lives to adulthood. And in each part of the world, a unique combination of pandemic diseases contributes mightily to race differences.

PIGMENTATION AND NATURAL SELECTION

Differences in skin pigmentation are of practical importance, more melanin being protective against sunburn and chronic skin changes, but disadvantageous in cloudy Northern climates unless supplemental D vitamin is given. Dark-skinned newborn babies, moreover, require more intense light in the "phototherapy" to lower bilirubin levels (*J. Pediat.*, *77:*1098-1100, 1970), again indicating the importance of pigmentary differences from birth on.

In Texas, in South Africa, and in Queensland in Australia, skin cancer is more of a problem (cf. Blum, 1955, 1965). Mad dogs and Englishmen go out in the noonday sun, but the latter without terminal hairs (and with a far longer life span). This type of sun-seeking behavior is more dangerous to the Angles than to the canines. Blond and red-haired and freckled individuals are wise to carry parasols, to use suntan oil, and to eschew high-noon summer sun altogether.

Apart from the natural pigmentation of the unexposed skin, there is also the capacity to tan. This is an interesting and separate variable. Some blonds have it, to an extreme, and so may become a deep oiled-mahogany, striking against sun-bleached hair and whitened lashes. Some brunettes in turn lack the capacity to tan and so develop a roasted-red and never really dark appearance. Under controlled experiments, the capaciay to tan emerges as a separate factor. Those who lack it are well advised to select indoor sports and dim-light recreations.

Apart from skin cancer and becoming leathery-wrinkled under the stimulus of the U.V. range 2200-2800 Angstrom units, there is the matter of skin pigmentation, skin temperature, and sweating. While we are all equally dark in the near infra-red, and an I.R.-sensitive visitor from outer space would find us all equally "black," dark skins may heat up faster in sunlight and raise to the sweat threshold faster.

There is a polar-to-equator double gradient of increasing melanin content of skin in both Europe and Africa. Such a gradient exists, though less spectacularly, in Asia and the Pacific Islands, and, in a way, in the Americas too. It is incomplete in that the apigmentation of skin and eyes and hair in Northern Europe has no parallel in Siberia or the Eskimo North. Even in Sweden and Denmark and Finland, blond hair and blue eyes are not quite the mode, though obviously far more common.

Still, only a decade has passed since we began in earnest to measure skin reflectance at various wavelengths in different human populations. For most groups we had only descriptions, variously including tanning, ochre, sweat, and dirt. The testing instruments are portable, battery-operated, and yield not just measurements of skin "color," but more important, skin reflectance, and most important, melanin concentrations in the areas of skin unexposed to either sun and wind.

BODY SIZE AND NATURAL SELECTION

Among the many differences between races, variations in body size are especially conspicuous. In some groups males average close to six feet, and in other populations average male stature is nearer to five feet. The *fat-free* body weight of American males approximates 135 pounds (some go as high as 190 pounds), while the comparable *fat-free* weight in other groups may average as little as 105 pounds.

Large body size can be advantageous. It commands respect, it is helpful in wrestling and hand-to-hand fighting, and it is a useful adjunct in hunting big game. The bigger man can cover more territory, he is speedier, he can tackle bigger game and bring back larger cuts of meat. Not too surprisingly, the noted hunting peoples of North America and Europe have been tall on a world scale. Given large animals to hunt, size is adaptive.

But size and massivity have their disadvantages. Larger size requires more calories, merely to keep alive, as Americans, Dutchmen, and Englishmen learned in Japanese concentration camps. Larger size requires more calories to grow on so that the genetically large child is at a particular disadvantage when food is scarce. And the large man, while more efficient at heat regulation in cold weather, is less efficient in hot weather.

For small size, the advantages and disadvantages reverse. Size is of no advantage when tending a trap. The less food there is, the more advantages accrue from being sub-sized. On short rations the genetically small child has a better chance to live and come to maturity. In the extremes of heat, the small man is unquestionably favored, as is true also during violent exercise even at moderate temperatures.

The small peoples of the world tend to be found nearer the

equator, and there is a marked *negative* correlation between the
mean annual temperature and weight. As one moves southward
in Europe temperature rises and weight drops, as D. F. Roberts
(1953) has demonstrated for 116 different populations the world
around. The very lowest average weights (96-100 pounds) are
associated with mean annual temperatures of 70-82°F., the highest
average weights (in excess of 160 pounds) are associated with a
mean average temperature of 40°F. (Fig.14) .

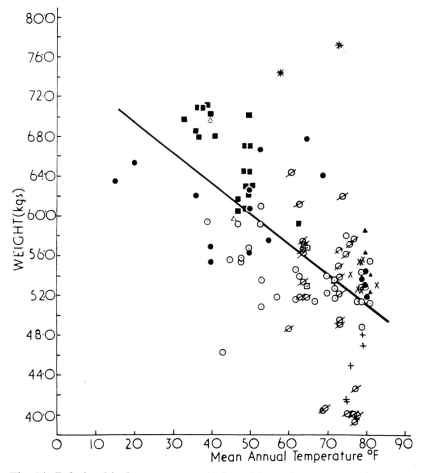

Fig. 14. Relationship between mean body weight and mean annual temperature. The higher the mean annual temperature, the lower the body weight
of population tends to be. (From Roberts, 1953, and Garn, 1960.)

As with any statistical association, the relevant variables are undoubtedly complex. Part is unquestionably physiological adaptation. Russell Newman (1956) has demonstrated for America that the colder the state of origin, the more fat young men have! Part is in all probability genetic adaptation to extremes of heat and cold with the little men stemming from lands that are hotter. And part may be attributed to genetic adaptations to nutritional extremes in the overcrowded, "underdeveloped" equatorial lands.

Famine is a powerful selective force, differentially eliminating the massive and large. Famine does not have to be a consistent part of the environment; one dies but once of starvation. In the face of continual caloric restriction, the genetically small individuals have a better chance to reach maturity and to reproduce themselves.

But how does selection make extremes of stature via hormones, enzymes, and bone growth itself? How does selection make pygmies, such as the Ituri Forest Pygmies? On the mechanisms by which pygmies are pygmy Dr. Robert Blizzard, Jr. writes as follows:

> State that pygmies do have growth hormone, but low insulin levels which are characteristic of patients with hypopituitarism. State that it has not been completely resolved whether these individuals make immunologically reactive, but biologically inactive growth hormone, or whether they have end organ resistance to normal growth hormone.

BODY-BUILD AND NATURAL SELECTION

Design a man for extreme cold and you have a virtual globule. Thick-set, reduced of leg and peripheries, there is a minimum of outstanding projections. By limiting surface relative to mass, less heat is lost by radiation, conduction and convection and (probably) by insensible perspiration. By pulling in projections closer to the warm body core, differential cooling is avoided with consequent danger of freezing.

Design a man for dry desert heat and he approaches paper-thinness. By maximizing surface relative to mass, heat loss by perspiration is maximized. Long hands and feet and a beaky bony nose, while contributing relatively little to the total cooling surface, are at no disadvantage where environmental temperatures are high relative to body heat.

It is not quite appropriate to bring in a variety of species for comparison, selecting perhaps the rotund seagoing mammals at the one extreme, and the linear desert fox at the other. Nevertheless, desert-adapted representatives of a species to tend toward linearity while related arctic forms exhibit a lower surface-mass ratio (Bergmann's law). And, in man, there is a distinct tendency for the more linear groupings to be associated with high (and relatively dry) environmental temperatures, and for the thickset populations to inhabit areas where below-freezing temperatures predominate.

Adaptations in body-build, however, involve more than just proportions, complicating the analysis of what we readily see and most easily measure. We must consider body composition, the amount of fat, and especially the thickness of the insulating blanket of outer fat. We must consider the location or "patterning" of the outer fat, which is subject to sexual as well as climatic selection. Fat over the cheekbones of Eskimos, even thin ones, and about their orbits, not only contributes to their flat-faced appearance but constitutes a protective mask as well. The stored fat on the rumps of Bushmen and Hottentots, an exaggeration of the typical hominid pattern, constitutes a particularly neat solution to two different problems. It provides a caloric reserve, an energy store for use during periods of food-scarcity, and being restricted in its location, least interferes with heat loss to the environment.

Variations in body proportions, in the amount and patterning of fat, and in other bodily constituents including the plasma volume and red cell volume, are not the only cold-climate and hot-weather adaptations. Each environmental stress is met by multiple and often different adaptations. But the racial variations in body build are more conspicuous, and we are beginning to learn much more about the "inner contours" of people of different races. Moreover, experimental studies are now going on to test the adaptive values of differences in body form and build, to verify the directions that natural selection has so often taken in shaping the shapes of man.

ADAPTATIONS TO EXTREME COLD

Of the climatic extremes into which man has voluntarily ventured, none is more quickly lethal (and therefore more selective) than extreme cold. Winter temperatures from minus 40° to minus 90° Fahrenheit are reported for various inhabited places in the Arctic. Without well-designed winter gear, such temperatures would be deadly in a matter of minutes. Even in full arctic regalia, frostbite and death by freezing are ever-present potentials. True, in the warmth of the snow igloo or sod barbara, such selection does not take place. But the very cultural advances that have made arctic living possible expose men to extreme outdoor cold selection to a degree that has never existed before the arctic way of life was mastered.

One obvious adaptation to cold-weather living is a minimum surface/mass ratio, with its obvious heat-conserving potentiality. A second involves size reduction in the limbs, particularly the legs, bringing them closer to the warm, central core. Both are characteristic of arctic peoples (Fig. 15). An increased thickness of subcutaneous fat would also be energy-conserving, as Baker and Daniels (1955) have confirmed. However, Newman (1956), working with draftees, has indicated that such a response may be largely physiological rather than purely genetic. Of the various cold adaptations known in mammals, the ability to generate more heat by raising the metabolic rate would be applicable to man, provided of course, that enough food is available. Evidence from a number of experiments favors enhanced metabolic responses to cold in Eskimos (Brown and Page, 1952) and in certain other groups.

Despite warm arctic clothing, the face is still exposed to wind and cold. The hands must be protected against freezing and must maintain their finer manipulative skills. Moreover, the peculiar Eskimo physiognomy (much more consistent across the Arctic than Eskimo serology) must also be noted in this connection. With fat-padded malars, fat-filled orbits, narrow eye-slits, and reduced nasal profiles, the Eskimo face fits the model of a cold-weather face. And a number of studies, like those of Brown *et al.*

(1953), confirm higher peripheral skin temperatures during cold stress (Barnicot, 1959). By implication at least, manual dexterity in Eskimos would be less impaired at low environmental temperatures. High-altitude natives in Peru also show increased peripheral blood flow.

It should be emphasized that studies on cold adaptation have so far been limited by technical difficulties, subject selection, and sample size. Laboratory experiments, moreover, fail to simulate natural selection where sheer survivorship rather than peripheral skin temperatures is the test of adaptive fitness. Nevertheless, the probability is that peoples long exposed to cold selection will exhibit, on the average, features and mechanisms of value in the cold.

ADAPTATIONS TO NIGHT COLD

In contrast to the Arctic and its far below-zero temperatures, minimal night temperatures at near-freezing levels (or slightly below) may seem unimportant. But such frosty situations command a very large part of the world, even the simmering deserts. And there are many human groups (quite recently some of our ancestors) who, poorly-clad, were in danger of getting their toes frostbitten as they slept. The problem of peripheral skin temperatures at moderate levels of coldness further relates to American Negroes, who apparently experienced more cold injuries during the Korean conflict than other soldiers.

Among the groups studied to date are the Alacaluf (the aborigines of Patagonia), desert-dwelling Australian aborigines, and Bushmen of the Kalahari. All exhibited the ability to sleep nude or partly nude, often using their clothing as pillows under conditions quite uncomfortable for Europeans. Generally, they exhibited an enhanced ability to raise their metabolic levels and thus generate more heat except for the aboriginal Australians. Peripheral skin temperatures tended to be higher than in European subjects under the same conditions (indicating greater peripheral blood fiow). Again, the Australians' adaptations were in the reverse direction (see Fig. 16).

Fig. 15A. Short limbs and a minimum surface-to-mass in the Eskimo (photograph, courtesy of the National Museum, Copenhagen). This illustrates *Allen's rule,* at one extreme. See *Readings on Race,* Chapter V.

ADAPTATIONS TO HUMID HEAT

A hot-humid environment is especially enervating, as we know in the sticky dog-days of summer. With moisture-saturated air, even below 100°F., the body becomes bathed in a continuous layer of sweat in an effort to reduce the heat load. In the tropics,

Fig. 15B. Increased limb length and a maximum surface-to-mass ratio in the Nuer (from Evans-Pritchard, 1940). This classic photography illustrates the working of Allen's rule where heat loss is adaptive.

there is attendant danger of excessive salt loss. If the body temperature rises too high, there is the possibility of death by circulatory collapse. Even apart from this extreme direction of selection, hot-humid environments would tend to favor individuals who can maintain a moderate work load in the water-saturated atmosphere.

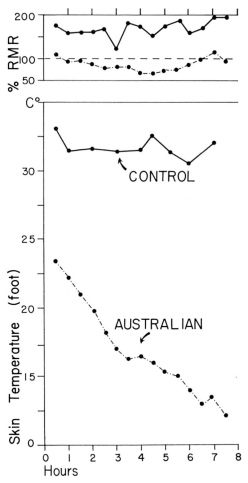

Fig. 16. Adaptation to moderate cold during sleep. In desert-dwelling Australian aborigines adaptation to near-freezing night temperatures involves a decrease in peripheral skin temperature. The marked elevation of the relative metabolic rate shown in control whites is not exhibited by the aborigines. (From Hammel *et al.*, 1959.)

For the existence of heat adaptations in man there is both direct and indirect evidence. The poorer cold adaptation exhibited by American Colored subjects in a number of studies would suggest that they are relatively heat-adapted instead. Paul

T. Baker (1958) compared colored and white subjects, carefully matched and acclimatized, and concluded that the former were better adapted to *humid* heat (but not to dry heat).

Assuming that the long-term inhabitants of steamy climes are the product of selection by humid heat, what mechanisms are at least theoretically involved? Dark skin color, by raising the surface temperature, could bring about sweating earlier. An increased sweating rate involving more sweat glands has been suggested but is currently the subject of debate as summarized by Barnicot (1959). A lower rate of salt loss is among the other mechanisms currently being studied. A fourth possibility, known for some desert animals, is the ability to tolerate increased heat loads.

Logically, the peoples of the African rain-forest and those of the Amazon basin exhibit adaptations to humid heat, though not necessarily the *same adaptations*. For both groups, of particular theoretical interest, the direct evidence is at present minimal.

ADAPTATIONS TO DESERT LIVING

Desert living is essentially a compromise, requiring tolerance of mid-day heat and night cold, tolerance of high ultraviolet intensities without increasing the heat load, and the ability to lose heat by perspiration while conserving precious water.

Desert mammals suggest several pathways to arid living, including nocturnal habits, leanness, and small body size. Only the latter two appear to be applicable to man, who notably ventures into the noonday sun. The early loss of subcutaneous fat in the Bushman may indicate its inadaptive nature under Kalahari conditions, and the Bushmen are notably small, as are many other desert peoples.

In theory, skin pigmentation should be moderate in desert men, enough to protect the malpighian layer, but not enough to build up the heat load. Baker (1958) has shown the disadvantages of extremely dark skin under hot-dry conditions. Thus the lighter pigmentation of the Bushmen may represent the theoretical compromise situation, a balance between competing directions of selection.

SOME RACIAL DIFFERENCES IN RESPONSES TO HEAT AND COLD

Author	*Sample*	*Findings*
Wyndom, McPherson and Munro (1964)	31 Australian aborigines 20 So. African Whites 7 Australian Whites	The aborigine has a much more sensitively adjusted thermal regulatory controlled channel between rectal temperature and sweat rate.
Wyndom, Metz and Munro (1964)	15 Chaamba Arabs 15 French Caucasians 20 So. African Caucasians	The Arabs display no greater adaptation to hot conditions than recent Caucasion inhabitants.
Scholander *et al.* (1958)	5 Australian Whites 6 Central Australian aborigines	Europeans maintained body heat by increased muscular movement during sleep.
Wyndham and Morrison (1958)	2 Unacculturated Bushmen 2 Europeans	No important differences found in response to moderate night cold.
Hammel (1960)	9 Alacaluf	Markedly increased metabolic response to night cold, persistent elevated BMR.
Adams and Covino (1958) see also Brown and Page (1952)	7 Negro soldiers 7 "Caucasian" soldiers 6 Anaktuuk Eskimos	Systematic Negro-white Eskimo differences in skin temperature and BMR during 2-hour exposure to cold.
Iampietro *et al.* (1959)	17 white and 16 Negro volunteers matched for body size and composition	Fewer rewarming cycles and lower finger temperatures in Negro subjects exposed to moderate cold.
Bass *et al.* (1959)	16 East Indians 16 U. S. Negroes 23 Chinese 17 U. S. Whites 8 Eskimos	Marked racial differences in plasma volume and blood volume especially for Eskimo of questionable relationship to climatic adaptation.
Baker (1958)	40 pairs of white and Negro soldiers matched for body composition and size	Negroes displayed a higher physiological tolerance to hot humid conditions, but heated up more under hot dry conditions.
Wyndham *et al.* (1952)	8 African mine laborers White data from the literature	Lower sweating rates, lower heart rates and lower rectal temperatures for Africans.
Riggs and Sargent (1964)	99 volunteers, Negro and white males, matched for age.	Negroes had lower rates of sweating, lower pulse rates; temperatures were similar. Capacity to withstand heat stresses greater.
Baker, Little and Thomas (1967)	42 Highland Natives, 10 lowland 8 USA/U.K. controls	Lowland-born F_1 progeny of high-altitude Indians show comparable peripheral blood flow.

A third area of desert specialization particularly exhibited by the kangaroo rat *Dipodomys* is the increased ability to concentrate urine. If man could follow the lead of this desert-living rat, he could conserve one to two pints of water a day, not a great deal compared to water lost in the exhaled air, but a saving nonetheless. No evidence exists at present for or against the possibility of increased urine concentration in desert man, a possibility further complicated by their largely protein dietary. However, there are two disorders in which urine is *less* concentrated than usual: the first is fibrocystic disease of the pancreas. Heterozygotes for this disease, therefore, would be less viable under desert conditions, and it is a safe bet that the gene involved will prove rarer in the hotter, dryer parts of the world.

The second gene-determined condition known to be unfavorable in the desert is the sickling trait (see Ch. VI). Peculiarly enough, the heterozygote *NS* has a reduced ability to concentrate urine and is therefore at an adaptive disadvantage where water is scarce (Keitel *et al.*, 1956). Needless to say, the sickling trait is uncommon in the less-watered parts of Africa and Saudi Arabia, in part because the heterozygote is at no advantage in such areas, and in part because the trait is disadvantageous where man's water loss is especially critical.

FUNCTIONING SWEAT GLANDS (FSG)

The two million or so functioning sweat glands (FSG) of the average individual make life possible in warm weather and hot. More sweat glands, or more sweat glands per unit of skin surface (FSG/cm^2) would lead to improved heat tolerance. Few sweat glands is clearly inadaptive (as in the congenital disorder termed ectodermal dysplasia). The number of sweat glands has been claimed to show racial differences. Kawahata (1939) reported fewer sweat glands in Ainu, more in Russians, still more in Japanese, and still more in Fillipinos (see also Rothman, 1954; Yoshimura, 1964, and Knip, 1969).

At the same time, one must consider the number of sweat glands per centimeter of body surface as an expression of differential growth. Starting with the same number of sweat glands, in infancy, the density per centimeter of skin surface would necessarily be less in adult males (who expand their surface more) and more in females. Similarly, well-nourished and dimensionally large people would be expected to have a lower adult sweat gland density simply because they stretch more. Hence, reported differences in the average density of functioning sweat glands related to skin surface (FSG/cm^2) may be complicated by the nutritionally determined magnitude of expansion and the total number of functioning sweat glands may therefore be of more genetic interest in the end.

SUMMARY

Increasingly, population differences in size, build, body proportions, and skin pigmentation may be viewed as adaptations to particular environmental extremes. Such differences often transcend geographical races, when similarly situated populations in diverse geographical areas exhibit similar adaptations to heat, humidity, or cold. Where migration has taken place, the distribution of such differences may provide a hint as to ultimate origins. But a particular climatic stress may not always be met by the same physiological adaptation. Cold can be met by increasing the caloric expenditure, or (to a limited degree) by reducing peripheral blood flow. Therefore, the adaptive nature of racial differences must be determined under conditions simulating the environments in which they have arisen, using fully acclimatized controls for study.

SUGGESTED READINGS

*Adams, T., and Covino, B. G.: Racial variations to a standardized cold stress. *J. Appl. Physiol.,* *12*:9-12, 1958.

Baker, P. T.: *American Negro-White Differences in Heat Tolerance.* H.Q. Quartermaster Res. and Engin. Command, U. S. Army Tech. Dep. EP-75, 1958.

Baker, P. T.: Racial Differences in heat tolerance. *Am. J. Phys. Anthropol.,* N.S. *16*:287-305, 1958.

Baker, P. T., and Daniels, F. Jr.: Relationship between skinfold thickness and body cooling for two hours at 15° C. *J. Appl. Physiol.,* *8*:409-416, 1955.

Barnicot, N. A.: Climatic factors in the evolution of human populations. *Cold Spring Harbor Symposia on Quantitative Biology, 24:* 115-129, Cold Spring Harbor, The Biological Laboratory, 1959.

Bass, D. E., Iampietro, P. F., and Buskirk, E. R.: Comparison of basal plasma and blood volumes of Negro and white males, *J. Appl. Physiol., 14:*801-803, 1959.

Blum, H.F.: Ultra-violet radiation and cancer. In Hollaender, A. (Ed.) : *Radiation Biology.* Washington, National Academy of Sciences, 1955, Vol. II, pp. 529-559.

Blum, H. F.: Skin cancer and sunlight. *Science, 145:*1339-1340, 1965.

Brown, G. M., Hatcher, J.D., and Page, J.: Temperature and blood flow in the forearm of the Eskimo. *J. Appl. Physiol., 5:*410-420, 1953.

*Brown, G. M., and Page, J.: The effect of chronic exposure to cold on temperature and blood flow of the hand. *J. Appl. Physiol., 5:* 221-227, 1952.

Ellinger, F.: *Medical Radiation Biology.* Springfield, Thomas, 1957.

Evanuk, E. *et al.:* Symposium-Arctic Biology: effects of extreme changes in light and cold. *Fed. Proc. Am. Soc. Exper. Biol., 23:* 1193-1221, 1964.

Hammel, H. T.: Response to cold by the Alacaluf Indians. *Current Anthropol., 1:*146, 1960.

Iampietro, P. F., Goldman, R. F., Buskirk, E. R., and Bass, D. E.: Response of Negro and white males to cold. *J. Appl. Physiol., 14:* 798-800, 1959.

Kawahata, I.: Counts of active sweat glands with human subject (in Japanese) . *J. Physiol. Soc. Japan, 4:*444-448, 1939.

Keitel, H. G., Thompson, D., and Itano, H. A.: Hyposthenuria in sickle cell, anemia: a reversible renal defect. *J. Clin. Invest., 35:* 998-1007, 1956.

Knip, A. S.: Measurement and regional distribution of functioning eccrine sweat glands in male and female Caucasians. *Human Biol., 41:*380-387, 1969.

Newman, R. W.: Skinfold measurements in young American males. *Human Biol., 28:*154-164, 1956.

Newman, R. W., and Munro, E. H.: The relation of climate and body size in U. S. males. *Am. J. Phys. Anthropol.,* N.S. *13:*1-17, 1955.

Riggs, S. K., and Sargent, F.: Physiological regulation in moist heat by young American Negro and white males. *Human Biol., 36:*339-53, 1964.

*Roberts, D. F.: Body weight, race and climate. *Am. J. Phys. Anthropol.,* N.S., *11:*533-558, 1953.

Rothman, S.: *Physiology and Biochemistry of the Skin.* Chicago, Univ. Chicago Press, 1954.

Scholander, P. F., Hammel, H. T., Hart, J. S., LeMessurier, D. H., and Steen, J.: Cold Adaptation in Australian aborigines. *J. Appl, Physiol., 13:*211-218, 1958.

Schreider, E.: Geographical distribution of the body weight/body surface ratio. *Nature, 165:*286, 1950.

Wyndham, C. H., Bouwer, W. v. d. M., Devine, M. G., and Paterson, H. E.: Physiological responses of African laborers at various staturated air temperatures, wind velocities and rates of energy expenditure. *J. Appl. Physiol., 5:*290-298, 1952.

Wyndham, C. H., McPherson, R. K., and Munro, A.: Reactions to heat of aborigines and Caucasians. *J. Appl. Physiol., 19:*1055-1058, 1964.

Wyndham, C. H., Metz, B., and Munro, A.: Reactions to heat of Arabs and Caucasians. *J. Appl. Physiol., 19:*1051-1054, 1964.

Wyndham, C. H., and Morrison, J. F.: Adjustment to cold of Bushmen in the Kalahari desert. *J. Appl. Physiol., 13:*219-225, 1958.

Yoshimura, H.: Organ systems in adaptation: the skin. In Dill, D.B., Adolph, E.F. and Wilber, C.G. (Eds.) : *Handbook of Physiology,* Section 4: *Adaptation to the Environment.* American Physiological Society, Washington, D.C. 1964.

VI

ABNORMAL HEMOGLOBINS, MALARIA AND RACE

For generations mankind has lived with malaria, or to be more exact, has lived despite malaria. Great sections of the world have proved unhealthy, malarious, poor places to survive. In both hemispheres, countries situated between 35° N and 20° S have been cradles of malaria, the "shaking ague." In Europe and the Middle East malaria had control of both sides of the Adriatic, much of the Italian coastline, Greece, the Ionian Island and Crete, and the shores of the Black Sea and the Caspian Sea. Since the malarial parts of the world, including the New World, were generally well-watered and usually densely populated areas, it is not surprising that in 1880 one half of the entire mortality of the human race was attributed to malaria!

In the areas of endemic malaria, in southern Europe and East Africa, it was observed that some few individuals did not acquire malaria, or at least did not exhibit the chills and recurrent high fevers, the enlargement of the spleen, and intestinal symptoms characteristic of the disease. Various explanations were offered, especially in the days when malaria was blamed on night air and exhalations of the marshes. Still, no really satisfactory evidence was offered as to whether immunity to malaria was natural or acquired early, whether it was due to some chance event (such as being unattractive to mosquitoes) or whether malarial immunity existed at all.

Rather recently, and as a by-product of studies on hereditary blood disorders, the existence of true natural immunity to malaria has been confirmed. Even more important, the relevant mechanisms have been discovered, and the disease of malaria has been shown to be responsible for several important directions of polymorphism in man.

THALASSEMIA AND THE MEDITERRANEAN

The story begins in the Mediterranean, and the word *thalassemia* comes from the Greek (literally "sea-blood"). The disease was first observed in peoples from the Mediterranean area, though it may actually be more common in Asia and not properly *"thalassemia"* at all.

Certain interesting features of thalassemia soon made themselves evident. The first, of course, was the Mediterranean distribution of the disease, especially (as noted in the United States) among individuals of Italian or Greek ancestry, but also among North Africans, Egyptians, and people from Asia Minor. Though observed elsewhere in the world (for example, Thailand) but rarely among Europeans not from the Mediterranean area, thalassemia is for practical purposes primarily limited to the Mediterranean and Irano-Mediterranean local races of the European Geographical Race (see Ch. XI), and to local races in India. Thalassemia also exists in Southeast Asia.

THE MECHANISM OF THALASSEMIA*

Clinical status	Genotype	Clinical picture	Hemoglobins
Normal	Homozygote normal	Within normal limits for hemoglobin and cellular fragility	Normal, slight amount of fetal hemoglobin
Thalassemia minor	Heterozygote	Slight anemia, increased osmotic pressure of the red cells	slight amount of fetal hemoglobin
Thalassemia major	Homozygote	Marked anemia, abnormal red cells fragile and increased osmotic pressure	Hemoglobin primarily of fetal type, little normal hemoglobin

*From Ingram and Stretton (1959), Neel (1949, 1950).

Family-line studies show that thalassemia is hereditary and that parents of a person with thalassemia major are "carriers" of the disease and exhibit thalassemia minor. Thalassemia is inherited as a dominant with thalassemia minor the heterozygotic state and thalassemia major the homozygotic. From the observed incidence of the disorder it is possible to calculate the gene frequency which ranges from nearly zero in Switzerland and northward in Europe to 0.20 or more in certain areas of Cyprus and northern Italy. For much of Italy, where epidemiological data is quite complete, frequencies for thalassemia average under 0.02, from 0.02 to 0.06 in Sicily and Corsica, 0.10 in the coastal area northeast of Bologna, and 0.18 in the Ferrara region.

THE GENETICS OF THALASSEMIA

Epidemiological and family-line data together confirm the existence of thalassemia as simply inherited in the form of a Mendelian dominant and with gene frequencies exceeding 0.02 and sporadically as high as 0.20 in the Mediterranean coastal area. Biochemical studies on the blood of individuals suffering from thalassemia major (the homozygotes) and other studies on the heterozygotic individuals suggest that the defect is primarily in the ability to produce normal adult hemoglobin A. Thus, the blood of sufferers from severe Cooley's anemia is almost entirely of the fetal type (or possibly of the A_2 hemoglobin subtype) while in thalassemia minor, the proportion of fetal hemoglobin is low. In short, the homozygotes cannot produce adequate amounts of the normal adult hemoglobin A, and their symptoms are largely referable to this gene-determined hemoglobin deficiency.

In terms of hemoglobin synthesis, there are at least two major thalassemia groupings. In one form, called beta thalassemia, the homozygote synthesizes little or no *beta* chains, and hence little or none of the "normal" hemoglobin A. Instead there is continued synthesis of hemoglobin F, in some cells, and prolonged survival of these cells. In the second form, alpha thalassemia, *alpha* chains are suppressed in the homozygote, and this is incompatible with life, since alpha chains are necessary for all functional hemoglobins. For a review of the thalassemia syndromes, see *Pediatric Currents, 5:*10 and *6:*19, 1970.

It must be noted that the individuals homozygous for the abnormal hemoglobin, that is, sufferers from thalassemia major, rarely reach reproductive age. In fact, Neel (1950) doubts whether the homozygotes could reproduce even if they lived to the child-bearing period. This lethality obviously eliminates some proportion of the thalassemia genes in every generation.

THALASSEMIA AND MALARIA

The clinical and geographical data on thalassemia raised two important problems, one being the origin of the abnormal gene (and its seeming restriction to the Mediterranean) and the other being its continuance in time. From the wide distribution of the gene on both shores of the Medterranean, an ancient origin could be postulated—prior to the spread of the Mediterranean local race as early as 5000 B.C. However, the absence of thalassemia in parts of Europe where Mediterraneans have migrated remained a puzzling feature. Even more peculiar was the continuation of the abnormal gene. Since, in each generation, a certain proportion of the abnormal genes are lost, the mutation would ordinarily be expected to remain at a low level—balanced only by new mutant genes.

What, then, explains the continuation of the abnormal gene, and its exceptionally high incidence in Crete, Bologna, and Corsica? One explanation would be an increased fertility in heterozygotes, but such increased fertility has not been found and could not explain known "island" of thalassemia. Similarly, an abnormally high mutation rate for the thalassemic gene, though postulated, has not been found, and again would not explain the marked variations in the incidence of thalassemia in Italy, Greece, and elsewhere from Iran to South China.

Beginning in 1950, however, a number of workers pointed to the correspondence between the distribution of thalassemia and the incidence of malaria. In those parts of Europe where malaria was holoendemic, that is, a severe problem the year round, thalassemia frequencies were highest. In the cold-climate and higher areas, thalassemia frequencies drop to near zero. Working in Sardinia, Cepellini (1955) has shown a far higher incidence of thalassemia in low-lying regions where malaria is holoendemic than in corresponding villages at higher altitudes. The emerging picure, and one now well supported by findings on the sickle-cell disease which follows, is that the thalassemic gene affords protection against malaria.

In a malarial region the homozygotes for thalassemia die early without reproducing. The "normal" homozygotes are afflicted with malaria and frequently die early, while the heterozygotes are somewhat protected and thus the continuance of both genes is assured. This simple explanation fits the data, explains the non-uniform distribution of thalassemia in the Mediterranean, and makes the race-limited nature of thalassemia comprehensible in terms of natural selection in malarial areas.

SICKLE-CELL DISEASE

A second hereditary blood disorder, primarily African in its distribution, is called sickle-cell anemia, after the characteristic appearance of the red blood cells in saline solution. As with thalassemia, sickling is inherited as a Mendelian dominant and there are two forms—the mild sickle-cell *trait* (the heterozygotic state) and the severe sickle-cell *disease* (the homozygous state).

The inheritance of sickling was confirmed by Neel in 1949 who demonstrated that individuals with sickle-cell *disease* were invariably the offspring of two parents with the sickle-cell *trait*. The molecular nature of sickling, in turn, was reported by Linus Pauling in the same year and the existence of a number of abnormal hemoglobins was subsequently discovered by Neel and his associates. Briefly, the individual homozygous for the sickle-cell trait produces the abnormal hemoglobin S (or some other abnormal hemoglobin) which has less oxygen-containing ability than the normal hemoglobin A. In a typical East African population, as in the American Colored population, there are three genotypes—the homozygous "normals," the heterozygous individuals with the sickle-cell trait, and those homozygous for the abnormal hemoglobin, exhibiting the sickle-cell disease (Fig. 17).

In Africa, frequencies of the sickling trait vary widely from zero in some areas to as high as 40% in other areas. Initially, these marked variations were explained in area-incidence terms (assuming the origin of the gene in the areas of highest concentrations) or by postulating migrations from high-sickling areas to low-sickling areas. Such explanations, reminiscent of racial anthropology of the last century and early explanations given for variations in the blood-group frequencies, put maximum weight on

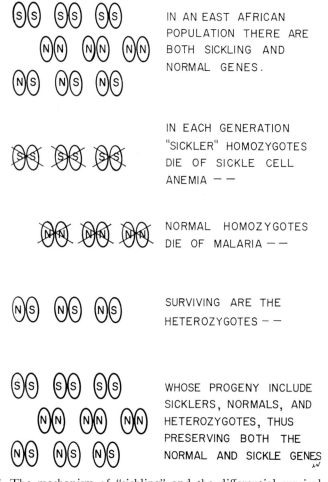

IN AN EAST AFRICAN
POPULATION THERE ARE
BOTH SICKLING AND
NORMAL GENES.

IN EACH GENERATION
"SICKLER" HOMOZYGOTES
DIE OF SICKLE CELL
ANEMIA — —

NORMAL HOMOZYGOTES
DIE OF MALARIA — —

SURVIVING ARE THE
HETEROZYGOTES — —

WHOSE PROGENY INCLUDE
SICKLERS, NORMALS, AND
HETEROZYGOTES, THUS
PRESERVING BOTH THE
NORMAL AND SICKLE GENES

Fig. 17. The mechanism of "sickling" and the differential survival of individuals with the sickling trait where malaria is a severe problem.

hypothetical migrations and minimum weight on purely local, epidemiological factors.

However, as with thalassemia, there had to be a more dynamic explanation for both the continuance and the peculiar distribution of the sickle-cell trait than migration theory offered. Since the sickle-cell disease is usually lethal, and since there is a differential elimination of individuals with the sickle-cell *trait* (cf.

Raper, 1949), some selective advantage had to maintain the sickling gene. A number of workers, among them Allison (1954), noted the geographical association between malaria and sickling (Fig. 18.) and postulated an adaptive advantage for the heterozygote in malarial areas. This postulate has now been well documented in a number of ways as reviewed by Allison in 1955.

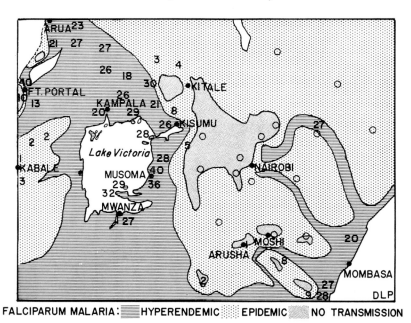

FALCIPARUM MALARIA: ▨HYPERENDEMIC ░EPIDEMIC ▒NO TRANSMISSION

Fig. 18. Association between the frequency of the sickle-cell trait in East Africa (designated by the percentages drawn on the map) and the prevalence of malaria (as shown by stippling). Where malaria is hyperendemic the percentage of sicklers is highest. (Redrawn from Allison, 1955, and reprinted from *Reading on Race*, p. 200.)

By now, the selection advantage attached to the sickling heterozygote has been confirmed, particularly by investigating children in African areas of hyperendemic malaria. In such areas, the homozygous *normals* develop malaria early, many die, and the vitality of the survivors is impaired. Those individuals homozygous for the sickle-cell trait develop sickle-cell disease with consequently increased mortality. The heterozygous sicklers, however, those with the sickle-cell trait but not the disease, are in effect protected. The incidence of malarial infestation is less, Heterozygotes develop malaria—but to a milder degree and with fewer effects particularly during pregnancy (Allison, 1955).

Thus, sickle-cell disease in Africa, like thalassemia in the Mediterranean (and in Greece where both are found) is an example of adaptive polymorphism in man. Both the normal gene, which serves to elaborate hemoglobin A, and the abnormal gene, which is responsible for hemoglobins S, etc., continue to exist in Africa because the heterozygote is at an adaptive advantage. The more common malaria is, the higher the gene frequency for sickling, reaching toward 0.50 as a maximum. But in areas where there is no malaria, or where malaria has come under control (as in western Europe and the United States), the heterozygote is at no advantage. Thus DDT, marsh drainage, screens, mosquito repellents, and antimalarials will eventually reduce the incidence of the sickling gene.

It will be noted that the sickle-cell trait in Africa transcends the conventional boundaries of African local races. Even within related populations, the incidence of sickling may be far higher in one group than in another. To some extent, these local differences may be due to the presence of other abnormal hemoglobins (C, E, etc.). But the greater part of the diversity is more easily attributed to purely local factors, chief among them the prevalence of malaria. Confirmatory evidence comes from Saudi Arabia where the incidence of sickling is far higher among oasis-village dwellers than among the hill tribes from whence these same villagers stemmed. All of this adds to the mounting evidence that the genetic makeup of any population strongly reflects the conditions under which it lives.

CULTURE, MALARIA AND THE SICKLE-CELL TRAIT

While the relationship between malaria and hemoglobins is quite clear in Africa, the existence of malaria itself poses a certain problem. Much of Africa is not naturally malaria territory: in its pristine state Africa offered few places for the mosquito *Anopheles gambiae* to breed. Only where the rain forest has been opened up by primitive agricultural practices (or in modern rubber plantations) does *A. gambiae* have a chance to spread. In the rain forest, or on the shaded forest floor, the malaria-carrying mosquito does not breed, and in the untouched rain forest malaria does not exist.

Reviewing such information, Frank B. Livingstone (1958) has concluded that malaria is of recent introduction in West Africa, following the spread of slash-and-burn agriculture, the opening of the forest floor, and the appearance of stagnant but not shaded pools for the carrier mosquito to breed in. Man made Africa malarial by providing the kind of climate the *Anopheles gambiae* mosquito needs and by raising the human population density to the point where there were always new individuals to infect and thus spread the chain of malaria. The dissemination of malaria in Africa would thus follow the spread of slash-and-burn agriculture and the abnormal hemoglobin-S would thus become adaptive in its wake. Sickling frequencies, particularly in West Africa, apparently bear this hypothesis out; peoples still pre-agricultural or late in attaining agriculture have the lowest incidence of sickling.

CULTURE, MALARIA AND THALASSEMIA

Livingstone has suggested that man paved the way for malaria in Africa; by cutting clearings in the jungle, man gave *A. gambiae* a place to breed, and the resulting spread of malaria put an adaptive premium on the otherwise inadaptive hemoglobin-S. This would appear to be the first concrete example of the way culture, that is, learned behavior, is capable of bringing about genetic change within populations.

The man-mosquito-malaria relationship in West Africa inevitably suggests a review of man and malaria in the Mediterranean. Seemingly, Sicily, Sardinia, the Po valley, and Cyprus have no immediate parallel with Africa. There were no jungles to cut down, and while there has been deforestation in some areas, swamps such as the Pontine marshes can hardly be considered as recent human artifacts except by silting-up of rivers.

Nevertheless, while man did not create the wet, humid marshy lands of the Mediterranean, he certainly did move into them for the practice of lowland agriculture. The early civilizations of the ancient world grew up along rivers with their seasonal floods and consequent stagnant pools. Oasis villages (where malaria is holo-endemic even today) provided the basis for early stable populations. Primitive ditch-irrigation, wheel-and-bucket watering, and crops specifically adapted to seasonal flooding supported the bulk of the populations. The consequent food surpluses make large population densities possible and vastly increase the numbers of people subjected to malarial selection.

SUMMARY

In the Mediterranean area through to Iran, and in a broad area of Africa, there are two distinct hereditary blood disorders that are irrevocably linked to malaria.

Thalassemia (or Cooley's anemia) is a hereditary disease, a minor disadvantage in the heterozygote (thalassemia minor) but lethal in the homozygote (thalassemia major). The rather high gene frequency for thalassemia in the southern Mediterranean appears to be maintained by malaria, generation after generation.

The sickle-cell trait (involving the abnormal hemoglobin-S) similarly reflects adaptive polymorphism. In malarial areas of Africa the normal homozygote and the abnormal heterozygotes are both at a disadvantage; the heterozygote has peak adaptive fitness where malaria is holoendemic.

In all likelihood the spread of malaria in Africa, and therefore the abnormal hemoglobins, was brought about by man's opening the forest roof by slash-and-burn agriculture. In the Mediterranean, lowland agriculture may have maximized population exposure to malarial selection. In both regions changes in the genetical makeup of populations can clearly be attributed to particular cultural practices.

In similar fashion, hemoglobin C in West Africa and hemoglobins D and E in Asia appear to be maintained by malarial selection. Altogether, the various abnormal hemoglobins and the retention of the juvenile type represent situations where a reduction in vigor is the genetic price paid for (antimalarial) protection.

The abnormal hemoglobins are so strongly associated with malaria, and glucose 6 phosphate dehydrogenase deficiency too, as to make the circumstantial case, notwithstnding the different vectors of malaria, the different genes, and the different responses. But the abnormal hemoglobins and red-cell G6PD deficiency can vanish in a millenium. Five thousand years of positive selection for hemoglobin S or G6PDD may be negated in one-tenth that time once malarial selection is eliminated.

SUGGESTED READINGS

Allison, A. C.: Protection afforded by sickle cell trait against subtertian malarial infection. *Brit. Med J., 1:*290-292, 1954.

Allison, A. C.: The distribution of the sickle-cell trait in East Africa and elsewhere and its apparent relationship to the incidence of subtertian malaria. *Tr. Roy. Soc. Trop. Med. and Hygiene, 48:*312-318, 1954.

*Allison, A. C.: Aspects of polymorphism in man. *Cold Spring Harbor Symposia on Quantitative Biology, 20:*239-255, Cold Spring Harbor, The Biological Laboratory, 1955.

Ceppellini, R.: The usefulness of blood factors in racial anthropology. *Am. J. Phys. Anthropol.,* N.S. *13:*389 (abstract) 1955.

Ingram, V. M., and Stretton, A. O. W.: Genetic basis of the thalassaemia diseases. *Nature, 184:*1903, 1909, 1959.

*Livingstone, F. B.: Anthropological implications of sickle-cell gene distribution in West Africa. *Am. Anthropol., 60:*533-562, 1958.

Livingstone, F. B.: The wave of advance of an advantageous gene. *Human Biol., 32:*197-202, 1960.

Neel, J. V.: The inheritance of sickle-cell anemia. *Science, 110:*64-66, 1949.

Neel, J. V.: The population genetics of two inherited blood dyscrasias in man. *Cold Spring Harbor Symposia on Quantitative Biology, 15:*141-158, Cold Spring Harbor, The Biological Laboratory, 1950.

Pauling L., Itano, H. A., Singer, S. J., and Wells, I. C.: Sickle-cell anemia, a molecular disease. *Science, 110:*543-548, 1949.

Raper, A. B.: Sudden death in sickle-cell disease. *E. Afr. Med. J., 26:* 14-22, 1949.

Raper, A. B.: Malaria and the sickling trait. *Brit. Med. J. 1:*1186-1189, 1955.

---

*Reprinted in *Readings on Race.*

For further references on the racial distributions of various hemoglobin variants, see Chapter XIII.

VII

RACE AND DISEASE

SINCE RACES are natural units, reproductively isolated from each other and with separate evolutionary histories through time, it is not surprising that they differ from each other in a great many gene-determined respects. Considering the unique history behind each race and the geographical and ecological uniqueness of its successive homelands, lack of differentiation would be remarkable indeed. Particularly in the random loss or chance acquisition of genes, each race represents a cumulative succession of accidents that could never be duplicated in millions of years.

These statements about racial differentiation, applicable to the "normal" genes commonly considered, pertain to abnormal or disease genes equally well. For the rare diseases, represented by but few carriers even in large populations, chance events could be prepotent. At a gene frequency of 0.01, 0.001 or even less, chance might easily eliminate a disease gene in one population while doubling or even tripling its frequency in a second. In one breeding population, the requisite disease mutation might never have happened, while in yet another population that mutation could have taken the form of a run.

Checking upon gene frequencies for rare diseases is at present no easy task. In most areas of the world, lacking hospital facilities and diagnostic skills, population comparisons are impossible. Even in the great medical centers, rare hereditary disorders may easily be missed, while other disorders may erroneously be considered race-limited or population-limited in their stead. Obviously, even elementary data on the comparative frequencies of the rare gene-determined disorders are to a large extent lacking today.

Nevertheless, there are numerous genetic disorders, either rare or lacking in most populations, that reach major proportion in a few groups. The sickle-cell trait, mentioned in the previous chapter with its counterpart sickle-cell anemia, is one example, as is

Mediterranean anemia (thalassemia major). For these gene-determined diseases, with frequencies close to zero in most parts of the world, trait frequencies reach 0.2 to 0.4 in a few restricted areas. In both examples the abnormal gene is maintained because the heterozygote is at an adaptive advantage.

A second class of disorders almost unknown in most parts of the world, but uniquely common in one restricted area, is increasingly coming to our attention. One of these unique diseases is *Kuru,* an extraordinary viral neurological disorder apparently restricted to Eastern New Guinea. A similar apparently population-limited neuromuscular heredofamilial disease has been reported from the Trust territory. In the Mediteranean area, *familial Mediterranean fever* and *Favism* are not only population-limited but promise to become included, along with the abnormal hemoglobins, among the conditions clearly adaptive in the heterozygotic state.

The third category, that of genetic diseases rare even in the populations that have them, is beginning to yield information. *Leprechaunism* appears to be an "Irish" disease, in that most known cases are of Irish origin or descent. *Tay-Sachs* disease and *familial dysautonomia* are probably "Jewish" diseases. The most economical explanation, that of genetic drift, probably explains these population-limited disorders. However, there are beginning suspicions that natural selection is also at work. By way of example, differences between the Ashkenazic (European) Jews and the Sephardic (Spanish-Portuguese and North African) Jews suggest that local environmental factors are important even with respect to the really rare hereditary diseases. One can easily understand how a disorder such as *congenital ectodermal dysplasia,* where sweat glands are largely lacking, would be more likely to survive in Stockholm than in Salerno.

Mutations being what they are, no disease can be considered to be entirely race-limited. The same abnormal hemoglobin that protects Italians in malarial areas also exists in Burma. The gene for familial dysautonomia probably also exists in some Moslem, Shinto, and Buddhist groups, but so far the disease has been reported mostly among Jews. Nor should similarities in the occurrence of rare hereditary disorders necessarily indicate common ancestry. The distribution of the sickling gene in Africa, Madagascar, Yemen, and Saudi Arabia we know now to be influenced by environmental selection. Thus, similarities between races in the same ecological zone, traditionally attributed to admixture, are often due to common directions of selection.

KURU: NATURAL SELECTION AND SORCERY

Our first example is *Kuru,* a remarkable disease apparently limited to the Eastern Highlands of New Guinea. Unknown to medical science until 1953, and quite unstudied until 1957, Kuru is well described by its pidgin-English name "skin-Guria" meaning shaking. Kuru is a progressive and incurable neurological disorder. Within a year after the onset of symptoms, the afflicted individual ordinarily dies.

Typically, the first sign of Kuru is incoordination. The victim begins to stumble, then increasingly he becomes less able to walk, and involuntary tremors become more and more common. Soon he is no longer able to sit, and speech becomes unintelligible. Next the abilities to swallow food, to urinate, and to defecate are no longer under the individual's control. Commonly, the full course of Kuru is run in a year or less, but the complete progress of this disease may take as little as three months.

Peculiarly, Kuru is limited to one group in Eastern New Guinea, the Fore, and some neighboring people among whom Fore women have married. It is known that far more women than men are afflicted by Kuru, so that the female-male ratio among affected individuals is 14 to 1 or even higher through the third decade of life. Possibly 1 per cent of all Fore natives are suffering from Kuru at any time, and in some hamlets as much as 50 per cent of all deaths are due to Kuru.

In an effort to find a trace element, poison, or food deficiency responsible for the diseases, Fore food, Fore body paints, and even Fore campfire smoke were tested. No trace element or rare earth that could serve as a nervous-system poison has been found. Moreover, Fore men living on Government dietaries outside of the Fore area also develop Kuru, so that Kuru is not a nutritional-

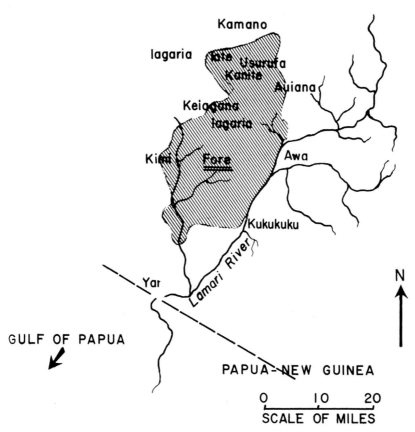

Fig. 19. The Fore territory *(shaded)* in Eastern New Guinea (redrawn from Gajdusek and Zigas, 1959). On one side of the Lamari River the disease of Kuru is not found. Though the genetic hypothesis seemed the most tenable, Gajdusek and his co-workers began the search for a slow virus by 1962 and found it in 1968.

deficiency disease. Kuru could be a genetically determined neurological disease, or a slow virus, or both, possibly transmitted by cannibalism.

Don't Eat People

From the beginning D. Carleton Gajdusek suspected a virus, "but conventional viral isolation procedures were all negative." He suspected cannibalism as the primary means of transmission "because the ususual practice of cannibalism as a mourning rite meant that the women and young children who disposed of the butchered bodies of their dead relatives were thoroughly covered with human tissue including brain and visceral tissues." Then in 1965, through to 1968, he succeeded in producing truly Kuru-like symptoms in monkeys and apes, finally transmitting the disease "from chimpanzee to chimpanzee, using bacteria-free filtrates, even from visceral tissue, and by subcutaneous and intramuscular innoculation." And Kuru is now a declining disease since cannibalism has begun to die out among the Fore, beginning in 1957. Still, a genetic factor seems likely, since sheep *scrapies* and the Aleutian mink disease both involve a genetic factor which determines individual susceptibility.

The sex-limited nature of the disease of Kuru may be explained by the sex-division of labor. Dismembering a Kuru victim was long woman's work. The familial nature of the disease may be explained by "taking care of one's own." The lack of direct person-to-person transmission may be explained by the fact that a slow virus is involved; the disease is definitely infectious but not contagious. In all of this the men remained aloof, engaging in cannibalism only in the case of a very close relative (say one's mother), and then only sampling muscle tissue, and then when cooked.

Portions of the entire Kuru story remain untested. No one wants to infect well people to confirm transmission in man. No one wants to test genetic susceptibility by controlled studies. But the genetic isolation of the Fore—the government-quarantine of the entire tribe (earlier reported in the *South Pacific Post,* May 24, 1960)—has ceased. It is bad to eat people, especially uncooked victims of Kuru.

Readings on Kuru

Alpher, M., and Gajdusek, D. C.: Changing patterns of Kuru. *Am. J. Trop. Med. and Hygiene, 14*:852-879, 1965.

Beck, E., Daniel, P. M., and Gajdusek, D. C.: A comparison between the neuropathological changes in Kuru and in Scrapie. *Exerpta Medica International Congress Series, No. 1000,* 213-218, 1965.

Gajdusek, D. C., and Gibbs, C. J., Jr.: Attempts to demonstrate a transmissible agent in Kuru, amyotrophic lateral sclerosis, and other subacute and chronic nervous system degenerations of man. *Nature, 204*:257-259, 1964.

Gajdusek, D. C., Gibbs, C. J., Jr., and Alpers, M.: Transmission and passage of experimental "Kuru" to chimpanzees. *Science, 155*:212-214, 1967.

FAMILIAL MEDITERRANEAN FEVER

The borders of the blue Mediterranean overlook a long coastline, long inhabited by members of an extended local race, with many micro-races. There, the great civilizations of the ancient world arose as well as the great religions of the Western World. And the Mediterranean area is rich in genetic diseases—hemoglobin disorders, red-cell enzyme defects, and *familial Mediterranean fever,* stemming from part of the Bible lands.

Genetically, familial Mediterranean fever is clearly due to a recessive gene, not a dominant as earlier suggested. Its distribution is apparently narrow, occurring "mainly in Armenians and Sephardic Jews," according to McKusick's summary (1966). As might be expected, clinical cases are more frequently observed in the progeny of cousin marriages, and it would appear that North African and Oriental Jews are most likely to be affected. Gene frequencies as high as 0.02 have been reported for some groups.

The disorder appears to be an amyloid disease, amyloid being a carbohydrate-peptide complex, developing in the first ten years of life, associated with fever, muscle pain, kidney involvement, and bone and joint involvement. It is progressive and largely lethal, and there is now question whether the disorder in Armenians is quite the same.

One of the earliest reports was given by Heller, Schar, and Sherf (1958), listing patients by place of origin, in which Libya,

Lebanon, Iraq, and Armenia predominated. Now some 900 cases have been summarized, according to a personal communication by Dr. Walter D. Block.

The disorder and its origin have an Eastern Mediterranean locale. It appears to be ancient. It may be an example of the "founder effect," but relatively high gene frequencies and hetero-zygote frequencies in some micro-groups suggest a heterozygote effect.

ORIGIN OF PATIENTS WITH FAMILIAL MEDITERRANEAN FEVER*

Stated Origin	Number of Patients
North America	67
Libya	25
Egypt	5
Israel	2
Syria	1
Lebanon	24
Iraq	22
Armenia	58
Caucasus	4
Turkey	14
Bulgaria	2
Greece	3
Italy	3
Spain	5
Not stated	18

*From Heller, Schar and Sherf ('58). See also *Brit. Med. J.*, 1:724, 1968.

Interestingly, among 73 Jews with this disease studied in Tel Aviv, not a single one was Ashkenazic (the group including most European Jews). Heller, Schar, and Sherf (1958) also observed that Sephardic (i.e., North African and Oriental Jews) contrib-uted all of the Jewish cases described by other authors.

The facts are not incompatible with the idea that the mutation for familial Mediterranean fever is an ancient one in the Medi-terranean as judged by its present wide dispersion. The mutation could well be 5,000 to 6,000 years old. The apparent concentration of the gene in the Eastern Mediterranean could be an indication of the site of origin, using the age-area approach, or it could be due to differential selection in the Bible lands.

Since the gene frequency of familial Mediterranean fever is low, well under 0.0001, the present limits may well be due to chance. However, since familial Mediterranean fever is definitely associated with impaired fertility, and a certain proportion of the genes are removed from the population in each generation, there is need to explain how the gene frequency is maintained. The fact that Ashkenazic Jews rarely exhibit the disease, while Sephardic Jews do, further requires explanation. A very likely possibility is that the heterozygote is at an adaptive advantage within the Mediterranean region, but not in northern, colder climes.

100 MILLION G6PDD'S

Further information on racial differences in physiology and disease came from testing synthetic antimalarials during and especially after World War II. Occasional individuals proved "sensitive" to the antimalarial drugs, that is, they developed hemolytic anemia due to the destruction of red blood cells. The characteristic symptoms were demonstrable in occasional individuals who had been given primaquine (a quinine-like drug), such common drugs as acetanilid (often used in cold remedies), and the sulfanilamides. A small proportion of individuals maintained on doses of primaquine or acetanilid exhibited drug sensitivity, but the vast majority of individuals did not.

When the proportion of drug-sensitive individuals was investigated in different geographical races, interesting results immediately appeared. The incidence of multiple-drug sensitivity in American "whites" proved to be low, 1% or even less. Among 1,000 prisoners treated with primaquine and described by Dern, Beutler, and Aving (1955) the incidence of sensitivity was 0.1%. However, a larger proportion of American Colored prisoners developed hemolytic anemia following the drug treatment. Among them, proportions of sensitive individuals ranged from 5% in one test to 11% in another group and 12% in yet another group. The true incidence of drug sensitivity in the American Colored population is therefore close to 10% as shown in the following table.

DRUG SENSITIVITY IN WHITES AND NEGROES

Group	Drug	Per Cent of Sensitivity
491 "white" patients	Sulfanilamide	1.3%[1]
131 Negro patients	Sulfanilamide	12.0%
1000 "white" convicts	Primaquine	0.1%
199 Negro convicts	Primaquine	11.0%

[1]Calculated by Beutler *et al.* ('57) based on data by Wood.

Primaquine and acetanalid drug sensitivity, and to some extent *favism* (see following section), are now known to be due to relative or total red-cell deficiency of the enzyme *glucose 6 phosphate dehydrogenase*. This enzyme is abbreviated to G6PD and the deficiency state is tagged G6PDD. The gene for G6PDD is X-linked, there is a wider range of deficiency states in females, and to some extent the most recent data favor the notion of partial X-inactivation (the Lyon hypothesis).

G6PDD has an interesting and informative distribution. It follows a primary broad band from the Mediterranean and the Middle East through India and Indonesia and into the Pacific, terminating in New Guinea. Rare in Central and Northern Europe (except among Middle-Eastern immigrants), it reaches a maximum of 60% in Kurdistani Jews. There is a second broad band in Africa, and together there is more than a circumstantial link to malaria. Earlier warmly debated (cf. Kidson and Gorman, 1962, and Allison, 1963), the malarial hypothesis continues to be the most reasonable one. Most recent studies do show that enzyme-deficient red blood cells are a barrier in the reproductive cycle of some malarial parasites. The absence of G6PDD in arid regions of Australia and its presence in oasis villages and well-watered towns in the Middle East puts G6PDD in the same class of interest as the abnormal hemoglobins.

According to an estimate by Motulsky and Stamatoyannopovlos, as summarized in Gardner (1969), 100,000,000 people are affected by G6PDD. But there are two forms of G6PDD, an African form (A) and an Asian and Mediterranean form (B). In the Asian and Mediterranean or B form, the enzyme is inactive in red blood cells of all ages. In the African (A) form, the molecule is active in some young red blood cells, but not in older ones. In Iran, according to Bowman and Ronaghy (1967), most affected individuals are B, as might be expected, but one or two per hundred are A. African (slave) admixture is considered the likely source of the A form.

So G6PDD emerges as a separate mutation, apparently responding to malarial selection and comprising at least two separate mutants, the A form in Africa and the B mutant form in the Middle East, Asia, and the Pacific.

FAVISM: WHEN GENE MEETS BEAN

Unlike primaquine sensitivity, which involves a man-made drug, *favism* is a natural disorder involving an allergic-like response to the broad bean *(Vicia fava)*. Susceptible individuals may develop severe hemolytic anemia by eating a plateful of the tasty fava bean ("broad bean") or even by walking through a fava bean patch in full bloom. The responsible agent lies in the bean and in the pollen, as Rosen and Scanlan (1948) reiterated.

Favism (the disease) has been known for three thousand years. Eating the fava bean was once tabu in ancient Egypt. The disease or disorder is largely limited to peoples of Mediterranean origin: Spaniards, Italians, Greeks, Armenians, and Middle-Eastern Jews. Favism is a variable disorder, it is sex-linked, and it is one of the few genetically determined food-borne disorders we know of now, except for lactase deficiency.

The fava bean and its pollen contain a substance which induces red-cell destruction in some (not all) individuals with G6PD-deficiency; hence the largely Mediterranean distribution of the disorder. But family-line studies in Greece and elsewhere suggest the workings of a second gene that determines individual susceptibility to the broad bean. The combination of G6PDD and the additional gene thus determines susceptibility to favism in the very areas where the broad bean (which requires a long growing season) is extensively used (cf. *Am. J. Hum. Genet., 18:* 253, 1966).

Favism thus appears to be a further but variant manifestation of malarial selection, in that glucose 6 phosphate dehydrogenase deficiency is one factor. The second or additional gene raises additional questions. Is it common outside of the Mediterranean but unexpressed in the absence of G6PDD, or is it, too, a gene that has some adaptive value where malaria was active as in the Mediterranean and the Middle East and elsewhere?

TAY-SACHS DISEASE: ON THE INCREASE

Tay-Sachs disease, named after the two separate discoverers, is an example of a rather rare, population-limited, genetically determined neurological disorder that begins in early infancy.

Like Gaucher's disease, Niemann-Pick disease, and amaurotic familial idiocy (A.F.I.), gene frequencies for Tay-Sachs disease are higher in European Jews than in their co-nationals.

Not only is the rare recessive gene for Tay-Sachs more common in European Jews than non-Jews, but it is at least a hundred times more common in Ashkenazic Jews than Sephardic Jews, and the gene frequency is highest of all among Jews from provinces along the old Polish-Russian border near Vilna. Homozygotes appear in 1 out of 500,000 non-Jewish births in the U.S.A. but in 1 out of 6,000 Jewish births.

Studies rule out both differential mutation rates and consanguinity as explanations, but favor a selective advantage in the heterozygote carriers. The gene appears to be ubiquitous, but apparently maintained and increased by a slight selective advantage accorded to the heterozygote—or is it slight? The recent calculations of R.F. Shaw and A.P. Smith (*Nature, 224*:1214-1215, 1969) postulate an increase in the disease at the rate of 7.5% per generation, large enough (they figure) to be observed in a single year!

LACTASE DEFICIENCY: NO USE FOR THE SUGAR OF MILK

Milk is an interesting and useful food. Most babies are addicted to it, many adults are too, and milk does provide quality protein at relatively low cost—cheaper in fact than steak. Not all adults can tolerate milk in quantity, however, because they lack sufficient *lactase* (the enzyme β-galactosidase) for the breakdown and absorption of lactase—the sugar of milk. Lactase-deficient individuals get abdominal cramps and diarrhea and are deprived of the lactose as an energy source if they drink much milk.

Lactase deficiency may be secondary to malnutrition and malabsorption, as in protein-calorie malnutrition, celiac disease, and so forth. Lactase deficiency may in some cases be the result of a previous milk-free diet, a common phenomenon for many adults in most of the world. Or, the deficiency of the enzyme lactase may be congenital, genetically determined, and population-limited, hence our particular interest here. In true adult lactase deficiency, lactose intolerance is not cured by improved nutrition and by gradually increasing the amount of milk in the previously milk-free diet.

A number of studies have shown lactase deficiency to be common in many parts of the Orient, and still other studies have shown lactase deficiency in Africans and in Americans of African descent (Bayless and Rosensweig, 1966; Davis and Bolin, 1967). Lactase deficiency is least common among adult Europeans and adult Americans of European ancestry, though some do have the enzyme defect associated with mild continuing diarrhea when they drink milk. So there are reasons other than traditional and economic as to why milk should be regarded as not quite fit for adults in much of the nonwestern world.

The key question is whether lactase deficiency can be shown to exist apart from intestinal pathology and after habituation to lactose. In one recent study, virtually all Thai subjects tested had abnormal lactose tolerance tests following ingestion of a lactose load. Continuing the load studies, fifty young Thai marines were fed 50 gm of lactose a day for an average of twenty-six days. Yet after this period of time, on a load equivalent to a quart of milk per day, they showed no significant increase in lactase activity (Keusch *et al.*, 1969). Most Japanese are lactase deficient.

Lactase deficiency is a complicated picture, and all adults have it to some extent, compared with infants, of course. Some sea-mammals have no lactose at all in their milk, and their pups are completely lacking in intestinal lactase. Some human infants are born without the ability to produce lactase and so cannot make use of human milk (which is very high in lactose) or cow's milk (which contains about half as much). Lactase deficiency is both genetic and environmental.

PHENYLKETONURIA

Phenylketonuria (PKU) is a genetically determined disorder in which the homozygote is unable to develop the enzyme *phenylalanine hydroxylase*. As a result, the amino acid, phenylalanine, is not converted into tyrosine, but to phenylpyruvic acid and other metabolites, which accumulate in excessive amounts, as does phenylalanine itself. Mental deficiency is the usual result unless the condition is diagnosed early and treated by dietary restrictions.

Among Americans of European origin, the gene frequency is approximately 0.01, and PKU appears in 1 out of 10,000 births. The frequency of the disorder in Japanese is perhaps a tenth as much, i.e., 1 in 100,000 live births (*Jap. J. Hum. Genet., 6*:65, 1961), and the frequency in American Negroes lower still, perhaps 1 in 150,000 live births, according to Reed (*Science, 165:* 762, 1969).

Since homozygotes died or were extremely impaired mentally, it follows that some selective force must maintain the relatively high gene frequency (0.01) in Europeans, and this selective force must be less effective in Japan and least effective in Africa. It may be noted that heterozygotes for the condition, the apparently normal recessive carriers, tend to show some elevation of both blood and urinary phenylalanine levels and that the partial metabolic block may be less of a disadvantage in light-skinned, fair-haired populations.

OTHER DISEASES AND RACE

A great many hereditary diseases are, for one reason or another, either race-limited or differ in gene frequency from race to race. Knowledge is best for the various abnormal hemoglobins, the two types of G6PDD, Tay-Sachs disease, amaurotic familial idiocy, and PKU. Cystic fibrosis also has its population associations, being especially common in Europeans.

Two possible reasons exist for the association between disease and population. One is the classic example of natural selection in which a particular genetically determined disorder is maintained because of the heterozygote effect. The abnormal hemoglobins are by now type examples, and it is clear that the recessive genetic disorder is a long-term genetic response to *Falciparium* malaria. G6PDD is probably maintained by malarial parasitization too, and such disorders as favism then become a complex genotype in which the enzyme deficiency and malaria are together part of the picture. It is very clear from the distribution of the genes that natural populations are involved and that present populations rather than historical trends are most closely reflected.

Genetically determined disorders may also be race-determined because of nonrandom factors, drift in the classical sense, the founder effect, the grandfather effect, etc. Here, the population-limited nature of the disorder has an obvious basis. The only problem is that of distinguishing between the chance buildup of genes and any degree of a heterozygote effect. Tay-Sachs disease could be the product of a random buildup or it could be an example of the heterozygote effect, the second being likely if, as claimed, the gene frequency is actually rising generation after generation and at a rate sufficient to detect increases within a single year!

There are many other disorders that are genetically complex, that differ in frequency from population to population, in part because of the total genotype. Cleft palate is especially common in Japanese (and these data are drawn from surveys of birth defects), but cleft palate is not a single genetic entity and in many cases is simply an obvious manifestation of other genetic or chromosomal disorders. So the relative infrequency of coarctation of the aorta in the American Negro (*J. Pediat.*, 74:623, 1969) is the opposite end of the picture, no longer attributable to poorer-quality epidemiological data, but a demonstrable phenomenon of still uncertain meaning. So too, the piling up of many defects in American Indians from the Southwest defines these populations in a certain way and leaves open the search for causes.

Now a disorder or disability may be race-limited simply because it is the product of still another race difference under certain circumstances. Negro pilots suffer vertebral fractures in ejection-seat accidents apparently because of the greater bending stress on their longer (or rather higher) lumbar vertebrae. American Negro women, in turn, may evidence less adult "osteoporosis" and fewer femoral neck fractures not because they do not lose bone but because, with greater subperiosteal apposition rates earlier, they have more bone to lose and they lose more slowly.

Now major chromosomal abnormalities should not be race-limited, and so far this supposition seems to be true. As far as we now know trisomy G, the XO, the XXX, the XXY, the XYY, and the XXXY are found without respect to race, creed, or national origin. On the other hand, there is evidence that minor chromosomal abnormalities and translocations, which become genetically transmitted, may bulk in particular populations and so tip the balance towards a greater incidence of minor congenital disease.

The data we have on race and disease are vastly incomplete. What we know is derived in part from special surveys in which entire populations are studied or from hospital data in which national origin, religion, or race can be identified or where names can be employed for particular inferences. Where such information cannot be obtained, it is to the patient's disadvantage and to the disadvantage of science as well. Knowing something about the ancestry of the parents or the origins of the patients, diagnoses can be made with far greater certainty, genetic counseling can be far more effective, and knowledge far more complete. Our present knowledge of race and disease has come about because such information is important and because the data can be assembled and because the records of specialists can be brought in for study and consultation.

THE ADAPTIVE NATURE OF HEREDITARY DISEASES

Such a disease as coronary heart disease does have a demonstrable genetic component, in the simply-inherited metabolic disorder *hypercholesterolemia. Hyperurecemia,* similarly inheritable, is one factor behind the painful disease of gout. Some proportion of diabetics are genetic diabetics, in whom the disorder may *not* appear in the absence of particular nutritional or emotional stresses.

The continuance of these obviously disadvantageous disease genes indicates either a high mutation rate, or better, some equivalent advantage associated with the genes. Since infectious diseases have long been with us, it is reasonable to look to them for the explanation.

Besides malaria, one may suggest tuberculosis, yaws, syphilis, leprosy, elephantiasis, and Bilharzia. In addition, there are the childhood diseases—measles, mumps, whooping cough, scarlet fever, diphtheria, and poliomyelitis. There are the ECHO and Coxsackie viruses, debilitating in the adult but often fatal in the newborn.

Within the past decades we have seen the rise of DDT-resistant flies and penicillin-resistant staphylococcus. Such genetic immunity need not be restricted to insects and bacteria. In fact, we have evidence that genetic immunity to toxins and bacteria does arise in man, and that some of the "hereditary diseases" represent adaptations to present or past epidemics.

SUMMARY

The investigation of hereditary diseases in different race-populations increasingly supports the contention that the genetic characteristics of every race are shaped by the environment in which it lives.

While purely chance events may be responsible for differing frequencies of very rare disease genes, gene frequencies of 0.1 and higher strongly suggest the workings of natural selection, and selection coefficients far higher than those considered plausible a few years ago.

Because of environmental differences, a particular heterozygote may be advantageous in one area and disadvantageous in another area, thus leading to differences between local races. However, local races from different geographical races may resemble each other in respect to particular gene frequencies if subject to the same direction of selection.

Extrapolating from such diseases as sickle-cell anemia, Mediterranean anemia, favism, and primaquine-drug-sensitivity, all race-limited hereditary disorders must now be considered as possible examples of adaptive polymorphism in man.

SUGGESTED READINGS

Allison, A. C.: Malaria and glucose-6-phosphate dehydrogenase deficiency. *Nature, 179:*609, 1963.

Bayless, T. M., and Rosensweig, N.S.: A racial difference in incidence of lactase deficiency. *J.A.M.A., 197:*968-972, 1966.

Bennett, G. H., Rhodes, F. A., and Robson, H. N.: A possible genetic basis for Kuru. *Am. J. Human Genet., 11:*169-187, 1959.

Beutler, E., Robson, M., and Buttenwieser, E.: The glutathione instability of drug-sensitive red cells, *J. Lab. and Clin. Med., 49:*84-59, 1957.

Carakushansky, G.: The lipidoses. In Gardner, L. (Ed.) : *Endocrine and Genetic Diseases of Childhood.* Philadelphia, W. B. Saunders, 1969.

Damon, A.: Race, ethnic group and disease. *Soc. Biol.,* 16:69-80, 1969.

Davis, A. E., and Bolin, T.: Lactose intolerance in Asians. *Nature, 216:*1244, 1967.

Dern, R. J., Beutler, E., and Alving, A.: The hemolytic effect of primaquine. *J. Lab. and Clin. Med., 45:*30-39, 1955.

Gajdusek, D. C., and Zigas, V.: Kuru. *Am. J. Med., 26:*442-469,1959.

Gajdusek, D. C.: Virus hemorrhagic fevers. *J. Pediat., 60:*841-57, 1962.

Gardner, L. (Ed.) : *Endocrine and Genetic Diseases of Childhood.* Philadelphia, W. B. Saunders, 1969.

Heller, H., Sohar, E., Gafni, J., and Heller, J.: Amyloidosis in familial Mediterranean fever. *Arch. Int. Med., 107:*539-550, 1961.

Heller, H., Sohar, E., and Sherf, L.: Familial Mediterranean fever. *Arch. Intern. Med., 102:*50-71, 1958.

Hernandez, F. A., Miller, R. H., and Schiebler, G. L.: Rarity of co-arctation of the aorta in the American Negro. *J. Pediat., 74:*623-625, 1969.

Keusch, G. T., Troncale, F. J., Thavaramara, B., Prinyanont, P., Anderson, P. R., and Bhamarapravathi, N.: Lactase deficiency in Thailand: Effect of prolonged lactose feeding. *Am. J. Clin. Nutr., 22:*638-641, 1969.

Kidson, C., and Gorman, J. G.: A challenge to the concept of selection by malaria in glucose-6-phosphate dehydrogenase deficiency. *Nature, 196:*49-51, 1962.

Knudson, A. G., Wayne, L., and Hallett, W. Y. On the selective advantage of cystic fibrosis heterozygotes. *Am. J. Hum. Genet., 19:*388-392, 1967.

McKusick, V. A.: *Mendelian Inheritance in Man.* Baltimore, Johns Hopkins Press, 1966.

Motulsky, A. G.: Metabolic polymorphisms and the role of infectious diseases in human evolution. *Human Biol., 32:*28-62, 1960.

Neel, J. V.: The study of natural selection in primitive and civilized human populations. *Human Biol., 30:*43-72, 1958.

Riley, C. M.: Familial autonomic dysfunction. *J.A.M.A.*, *149*:1532-1535, 1952.

Rosen, A. P., and Scanlan, J. J.: Favism. *N.E.J. Med.*, *239*:367-368, 1948.

Sansone, G., and Segni, G.: Sensitivity to broad beans. *The Lancet*, *273*:295,1957

Szeinberg, A., Asher, Y., and Sheba, C.: Studies on glutathione stability in erythrocytes of cases with past history of Favism or sulfa-drug-induced hemolysis. *Blood*, *13*:348-358, 1958.

VIII

RACE AND GENETIC DRIFT

Following inexorable laws of genetics, gene frequencies may be expected to remain constant from generation to generation. If the gene frequency for blood group O is 0.64 in this generation, it will be 0.64 in the next. If 18 per cent of Englishmen have light hair today, 18 per cent had light hair during Victoria's reign. Stability of gene frequencies, once panmixia is achieved, makes possible mathematical excursions into the past and prediction of future trends.

But gene frequencies do not always remain constant, thus changing the genetic nature of a race-population. One mechanism capable of changing gene frequencies is, of course, natural selection, which alters the balance of alleles in one direction or another. Mutation is a second mechanism that affects gene frequencies—introducing new genes into the population through mutating (i.e. changing) some proportion of the old. And a third evolutionary mechanism called *random genetic drift,* or more simply, "drift," is also capable of altering gene frequencies but in a random or nondirected fashion.

Drift, in fact, is largely statistical variation—purely random fluctuation of gene frequencies from generation to generation. As any student of statistics knows, frequencies or proportions will differ somewhat in successive sub-samples as a result of sampling error, that is, accidents of sampling. In successive human generations chance events may slightly lower a gene frequency, or raise it unpredictably and in no regular pattern (see Fig. 20).

Characteristically, genetic drift is of minimal importance in large populations. Where the number of individuals, or better the number of individuals of breeding age, is large, say 1,000 or more, losses of genes in some lineages are balanced by gains in others. In such a large population, random variations in gene frequency ordinarily will not exceed ± 1%. In small populations,

GENERATION 1

GENERATION 2

GENERATION 3

GENERATION 4

Fig. 20. The mechanism of genetic drift. In small populations or with low gene frequencies regardless of population size, the frequency of particular genes may vary considerably from generation to generation. Some of the differences between local races may be attributed to this process.

however, random variations in gene frequency may loom large. With a breeding population of but 100, a 5% increase or decrease in gene frequency may easily occur from generation to generation. In extreme cases, as where a particular gene is rare to begin with or where chance variations run in the same direction for several generations, a gene may be eliminated from the population on a purely chance basis.

Moreover, such small populations as have been described are by no means small as human groups go. An Australian horde may number 400, but excluding grandparents and children, the size of the *breeding population* is less than 100. For a Bushman band, and for some Eskimo isolates the breeding population may be ten or even less. One can easily imagine the fate of comparatively rare genes in such a population—either becoming eliminated entirely, or the frequency becoming "fixed" at 1.00, due entirely to chance events.

Thus it is that some students of human population genetics, among them Gabriel Lasker and Joseph Birdsell, have been interested in random drift as explaining some differences between some isolates, differences between micro-races, and even differences between geographical races. If a gene frequency became fixed at either 1.00 or 0.00 just at the time a particular isolate began explosive population growth, such a gene frequency might characterize the descendants, ultimately numbering in the thousands. And, for rare and uncommon genes barely represented in a population of any size, random genetic drift may well account for the population differences that we know.

There is much attractiveness in genetic drift as an explanation for some part of racial differences. After all, most human populations have been small; Pleistocene populations rarely exceeded fifty, equivalent to a breeding population of little more than ten. Neolithic communities of a hundred or so were equivalent to breeding populations of twenty-five. Only rarely, and not much before the present era, were populations larger than 2,000 practicable, and these populations were still "small" in terms of the number of breeding pairs.

As migrants migrated, they broke into small groups. The boatloads of Polynesians viewed by Captain Cook constituted small populations, ideal for the mechanism of drift. Eskimo groups of not more than fifty wandered from Russian Siberia to American Alaska and back again. Even the recent migrations into America have involved Lebanese clans, Irish towns, and Armenian villages. Such units, detached from the larger group, have undoubtedly been subject to genetic drift, as Bentley Glass has attempted to demonstrate for the "Dunkers," a religious isolate of German origin. "Drift" may account for some of the differences between Yemenite and Alexandrian Jews, or the Jews of North Africa and those of Poland or Lithuania.

Yet there are arguments against according drift too large a role in racial differentiation. Drift, being purely chance, does not distinguish between adaptive genes and inadaptive genes. Drift alone would pile up high gene frequencies for inadaptive genes, but such high frequencies would then be whittled down by natural selection. Drift could account for some differences between adjacent populations, but not differences that are distributed in a regular way, forming "clines." Only for perfectly neutral genes could drift operate along to bring about major differences, and at the present time we are increasingly skeptical of such neutral genes, as is evident throughout this book.

Nevertheless, drift could operate to lose a gene completely, and this may be the explanation for the virtual absence of blood group B in the Americas. Alternatively, drift in conjunction with natural selection could operate to speed up the direction of evolution. Given a half-dozen populations all subject to the same selective forces, the population in which drift and natural selection operated together would have the best chance of survival. In such a population the largest number of individuals would come to possess the optimum genotype, the fastest, and thus would soon outnumber the others.

Drift can now be investigated in two ways. It is possible to set up a computer program to determine the circumstances under which random genetic drift may have the maximum race-making potentiality. Alternatively, it is possible to investigate drift in small human isolates, over time, or in relation to the populations from which they have been drawn. While these mathematical and investigative techniques can indicate the theoretical importance of drift, the extent to which drift actually has been operative in bringing about racial differences is extremely difficult to determine. Moreover, a small degree of gene-flow from the outside could well counter the direction of drift, through its effect on the size of the total breeding population.

THE STUDY OF DRIFT

In the days when human population genetics consisted largely of ABO and Rh frequencies from large-city hospital records, the first "big picture" emerged, that of geographical clines of O and A and B and the Rh-negative blood type. Such data provided scant evidence for drift. It was a better testimonial for geography and for distance. But as attention was directed to natural human populations rather than blood-bank compilations, to single villages rather than megacities, as more blood factors were added to the studies, irregularities in the distributions became evident. Neighboring villages could be uncomfortably different at numerous loci. A chain of villages could show paradoxical variations in ABO, MNS, D, K, Inv, Hp, and Fy^a and Di^a polymorphisms. Or a single village might show frequencies quite out of line for the general geographical area.

Cavalli-Sforza, Barrai, and Edwards (1964) found differences in gene frequencies in neighboring villages in the Parma Valley of Italy. These differences they attributed to drift. Village-to-village differences in New Guinea, transcending language groupings, are now reasonably attributable to drift. In Greece, two villages within mere miles of each other "show a remarkable degree of heterogeneity in gene frequencies," according to Fraser *et al.* (1969). This, they suggest, may reflect a "founder effect," or genetic drift, or both.

OUR FOUNDING FATHERS AND THEIR GENES

As described in this chapter, an isolate, a community, and even an extended local race may have an unusual gene frequency at one or more loci simply because of random fluctuations that operated when numbers were small. Polygamy, the sororate, the junior leviate, and other possibilities that restrict mating combinations may enhance the actions of genetic drift. There is also a special case of drift known as the "founder effect," which describes variations in gene frequency due to chance events at the time an isolate is founded. Such a founder effect not only operates in theory, but there is splendid historical evidence for just such a phenomenon (Laberge and Dallaire, 1967, and Laberge, 1969).

The example in this case is hereditary *tyrosinemia,* which is responsible for liver damage and liver failure in early infancy and, if untreated, for early death. The place is French Canada in the Chicoutimi-Lake–St. John region of Quebec, between Lake St. John and the St. Lawrence River. In 1965 alone, twenty-nine cases were reported. It is now known that in the Lake-St. John–Chicoutimi area the gene frequency for hereditary tyrosinemia is between 2% and 4%, far higher than in Quebec Proper and in Ontario.

The relatively high frequency of tyrosinemia in the Lake-St. John–Chicoutimi area can be traced back to Louis Gagné and his wife Marie Michel, two of whose children (Louise Gagné and Ignace Gagné) are ancestors in direct line to the twenty-nine families, and now 1,650 individuals, that include the cases of tyrosinemia. This pair of old-world founders and two of their nine children introduced the gene into French Canada by 1644, and as their numbers increased so did the cases of tyrosinemia.

Using this kind of information as a type example, extending the thinking elsewhere, Livingstone (1969) suggests that the founder effect accounts for the relatively high frequency of Tay-Sachs disease in Jews from the Vilna area, and he calculates, by computer program, how a founder effect could be responsible for population differences in the frequency of cystic fibrosis and other hereditary diseases. Indeed, it is his suggestion and that of others that the founder effect, the special case of drift, may provide an alternative explanation for many situations where particular gene frequencies have been previously explained in terms of increased fertility of the heterozygote.

SUMMARY

Random genetic drift, the Sewell Wright effect, most commonly called "drift," may be considered as a third evolutionary mechanism responsible for racial differentiation. Drift operates at maximum effectiveness in small populations or at very low gene frequencies. Since most human populations in the past were small, ideal in size for drift to operate, this mechanism may explain differences between micro-races, local races, and even geographical races. Nevertheless drift could not operate for long in opposition to natural selection. Most likely, drift has been effective where it has conicided with the direction of selection in particular race-populations.

Special cases of "drift" operate where the founding fathers of an isolate initially, differ in gene frequencies from the parental population, or where a single lineage has attained numerical predominance in the course of subsequent generations, or where the Y chromosomes in a hybrid population are predominantly from one of the two parental groups.

SUGGESTED READINGS

Birdsell, J. B.: Some implications of the genetical concept of race in terms of spatial analysis. *Cold Spring Harbor Symposia on Quantitative Biology, 15:*259-314, Cold Spring Harbor, The Biological Laboratory, 1950.

Glass, B. Genetic changes in human populations especially those due to gene flow and genetic drift. *Advances in Genetics, 6:*95-139, New York, Academic Press, 1954.

*Glass, B., Sacks, M. S., John, E. F., and Hess, C. Genetic drift in religious isolate: an analysis of the causes of variation in blood group and other gene frequencies in a small population. *Am. Naturalist, 86:*145-159, 1952.

Laberge, C.: Hereditary tyrosinemia in a French Canadian isolate. *Am. J. Hum. Genet., 21:*36-45, 1969.

Laberge, C., and Dallaire, L.: Genetic aspects of tyrosinemia in the Chicoutimi region. *Canad. Med. Assoc. J., 97:*1099-1100, 1962.

Lasker, G. W.: Mixture and genetic drift in ongoing human evolution. *Am. Anthropol., 54:*433-436, 1952.

*Reprinted in *Readings on Race.*

*Lasker, G. W.: Human evolution in contemporary communities, *Southwestern Anthropol., 10:*353-365, 1954.

Lasker, G. W., and Kaplan, B. A.: The coefficienct of breeding isolation: population size, migration rates, and the possibilities for random genetic drift in six human communities in Northern Peru. *Human Biol., 36:*327-38, 1964.

Livingstone, F. B.: The founder effect and deleterious genes. *Am. J. Phys. Anthrop., 30:*55-60, 1969.

Wright, S. Classification of the factors of evolution. *Cold Spring Harbor Symposia on Quantitative Biology, 20:*16-24, Cold Spring Harbor, The Biological Laboratory, 1955.

Wright, S., Fisher, and Ford on "The Sewall Wright Effect," *Am. Scientist, 39:*452-458, 1951.

IX

RACE MIXTURE

T HROUGHOUT human history countless isolates have lost their reproductive barriers and in consequence their genetic uniqueness. Remote tribes have met and exchanged members of marriageable age. Larger groups have engaged in warfare, claiming women from the defeated as concubines and slaves. In the long course of human migration dozens of aboriginal populations have been swept up in the flood tide of population expansion, joining the winners genetically as well as politically. Victorious soldiers have not only contributed genes to the conquered nations, but through war-brides brought home have altered the genic makeup of their own groups as well.

In the days of foot-warfare and slow ox-teams and carts, admixture was largely between adjacent isolates. When the Israelites overran the Canaanites and the Philistines, they were among peoples much like themselves. Warfare among the Greek city-states or between the Romans and their Italic neighbors similarly involved micro-races or local races at most. But with the advent of well-supplied legions, with the introduction of navies, and with all means of rapid mass transport, admixture came to involve geographical races as well.

Today, we see numerous examples of crosses between disparate geographical races, with an increasingly larger proportion of the world's population so formed. Much of Central and South America is "mixed," Amerindian times European in origin, and often partly African. The American Negro is properly European times African as are the Cape Colored of South Africa. Hawaii has long encompassed European-Asiatic and European-Asiatic-Polynesian mixtures, and European-Asiatic crosses are increasingly frequent in North America and Japan.

Race mixture, whether between local races or geographical races, must be added to natural selection and drift as a race-making mechanism. Although race mixture does not add new genes (as mutation does) and does not of itself remove genes from the population, it increases genetic variability; it results in new genotypic combinations and thus provides new grist for the evolutionary mill.

THE GENETICS OF RACE MIXTURE

Because race mixture of any kind involves a union of separate gene pools, each differing somewhat from the other, the immediate effect of admixture is to increase genetic diversity. This is least true, of course, where isolates are very like each other in gene frequencies, and most apparent where previously separate groups differ largely in genetic makeup. In either extreme, however, increased genetic diversity provides more material for natural selection to work upon. Race mixture increases population variability and potentially at least, speeds up natural selection.

But race mixture is far more than the arithmetic addition of alleles. While making the new gene pool more complex than was true of either parental grouping, admixture also results in new genotypic combinations. As a simple example, suppose that one group contained the genes *a* and *b*, while the second group contained the genes *c* and *d*. In the hybrid population we would then find a total of ten different genotypic combinations, *aa, ab, ac, ad, bb, bc, bd, cc, cd,* and *dd*. Not only is morphological variability increased as a result of admixture, but new genotypes are thus produced (Fig. 21).

The existence of these new genotypes is particularly important, because natural selection operates upon genotypes rather than on individual genes, and the new genotypes may offer advantages not present in any of the parental genotypes. By way of example, the genotypes *bc* and *bd* may ensure greater cold resistance or superior heat resistance, or they may protect the possessor against a greater range of thermal extremes. In fact, the new genotypes *bc* and *bd* may be so superior to the original genotypes *aa* and *bb* or *cc* and *dd* as to result in a marked change in the genetic nature of the hybrids. In this event the products of admixture would eventually provide little clue as to the parental genotypes or to

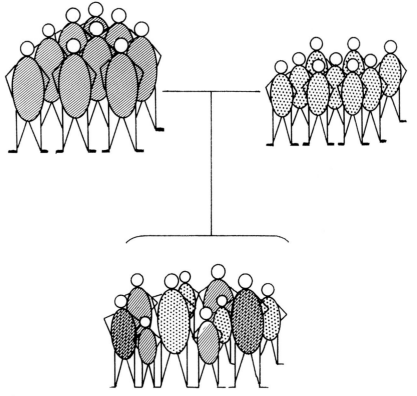

Fig. 21. Stick-figure diagram of race mixture. Although admixture ("hybridization") does not contribute new genes it does result in new genotypic combinations and in increased morphological and genetic variability and, ultimately, in new adaptive modes.

the proportions of each group that originally entered into admixture.

Were we to enjoy a long-term view of racial evolution in any part of the world, we would witness an almost rhythmic succession of steps. First there would be the isolates, each polished to a peak of adaptive fitness in its own ecological zone. Then there would be admixture, followed by increased genetic diversity, new genotype combinations, and ultimately new peaks of fitness. Again, there would be admixture and further selection among the new genotypes, leading to new adaptive peaks again and again and again. While we, with out birds-eye time-lapse view could see the creative power of admixture and the recurrent development of new adaptive modes, the populations involved would be conscious only of the short-term run of events. At each stage, and with a myopic view of history, they would loudly proclaim their own racial "purity."

RACE MIXTURE VIEWED AS HARMFUL

In the last century, race-mixture, or more specifically mixture between geographical races, was commonly viewed as harmful. Europeans, themselves the product of centuries of admixture between local races, took a dim view of the new race-hybrids their own expansion produced. Arguing on quasi-biological grounds, particularly with reference to the mule, impaired fertility was said to be one product of human racial miscegenation. Human "hybrids" of various sorts were claimed to be indolent, immoral, untrustworthy, and uneducable. Progeny resulting from race mixture were alleged to fall below the intellectual level of either parent race. Somewhat inconsistent, however, was the attitude toward Eurasians. As pictured in mystery novels as late as 1920, Eurasians were exceptionally sinister, sly, Machiavellian, yet capable. When a Eurasian entered an Edgar Wallace novel, shutters clanked, doors squeaked, and the heroine was tethered in a junk bound for Singapore with the pure-English hero in close naval pursuit.

Despite such novel views, human "hybrids" (that is, geographical race-crosses) have evidenced no signs of impairment. Population expansion in Middle and South America belies any diminution in fertility. No evidence exists as to reduction in mental acuity. Morality among products of race mixture has been neither lower nor higher than their station in life allows. In Hawaii (as elsewhere) Eurasians have not lived up to their reputation as sinister, but have contributed lively, useful, imaginative, and law-abiding citizens, many of them unusually attractive as the motion-picture audience has come to discover.

RACE MIXTURE AND HYBRID VIGOR

While exponents of racial purity were still arguing the biological inferiority of human hybrids and were suggesting reduced
fertility, impaired viability, and psychological instability as the
price of miscegenation, plant experimenters encountered a totally
opposite trend. Intentional plant hybrids, made by crossing distinct strains or "races," proved to be superior in fertility, superior
in growth, and superior in disease-resistance. This phenomenon,
still imperfectly understood, is the result of crossing genetically
distinct lines. Limited to hybrids, especially F_1 (first generation)
hybrids, it has been termed *hybrid vigor*.

One conspicuous example of hybrid vigor is hybrid corn. In
the field the stalks are taller and sturdier and the ears larger, more
numerous, and better filled. Hybrid tomatoes are another example: the premium "hybrid" seeds cost more, they produce
bigger and more vigorous plants and finer, firmer, better-fleshed
tomatoes. Intentional hybrids in other lines evidence greater disease resistance, and if well-fertilized, amazing productivity. One
explanation for this phenomenon of hybrid vigor is the dispersal
of deleterious genes in the F_1 generation. Notably, the advantages
are less obvious in the F_2 back-crosses, so that fresh hybrid seed
must be used at each sowing or planting.

Does hybrid vigor exist in man, in the first filial generation
from geographical race-crossings? Here we encounter an experi-
ental problem, that of controlled conditions. Whereas hybrid and
straight-line corn can be tested in the same field, under comparable conditions of temperature, rainfall, and fertilizer, such experimental controls have not been possible for man. Where can
we compare (except possibly in Hawaii) Asiatic, European, and
Asiatic-European crosses under comparable conditions of nurture?

Some few human populations have been offered as examples
of hybrid vigor. The tall, vigorous, but carious Pitcairners, descendants of the *Bounty* mutineers and their Tahitian wives, have
been offered as an example of hybrid vigor in man. But these liv-

ing Pitcairners are not F_1s, but complex back-crosses, primarily of one male line. In like fashion, the Norfolk islanders are not first generation hybrids. Something other than hybrid vigor, possibly natural selection, possibly adherence to a rather English way of life, accounts for the size and ruggedness of these descendants of the *Bounty* studied forty years ago by the anthropologist H. L. Shapiro.

Still, if "hybrid vigor" exists in man, we should be able to detect it under circumstances where environmental variables are well controlled. By way of example, growth studies of English and English-Negro infants in Liverpool orphanages may well provide information on hybrid vigor. Alternatively, instead of considering first generation geographical race-crosses we may investigate highly inbred human lines, where suppressor genes may limit size and growth. Then, by measuring the progeny of out-marrying members of such isolates, size increment due to "heterosis" may well be demonstrated.

Such an investigation has been conducted by Dr. Frederick S. Hulse. For his "inbred" population, he used members of isolated Swiss villages where cousin marriage was common. His "outbred" comparison group involved members of the same villages, who married outside of the village. And as shown below, the progeny of the out-marrying Swiss proved larger than did the children of the still-inbreeding Swiss. The experimental design, using intra-village and inter-village matings, shows how environmental circumstances can be kept relatively constant, thus avoiding the major pitfall of most attempts to uncover hybrid vigor in man.

BODY SIZE IN PROGENY OF ENDOGAMOUS AND
EXOGAMOUS SWISS MATINGS*

Measurement	Exogamous (Inter-village)	Endogamous (Intra-village)
Stature (cm)	168.5	166.2
Weight (kg)	73.4	72.0
Shoulder breadth (cm)	38.8	38.7
Head length (mm)	189.0	187.5

*From Hulse, F. S.: Exogamie et heterosis. *Arch. Swisses d'Anthropologie generale,* 22:103-125, 1957.

STUDIES ON RACE MIXTURE

Though there are obvious difficulties in the study of race mixture, chiefly arising from the lack of controlled conditions, there is much to be gained from such investigations, particularly in the area of human genetics. The mode of inheritance of many human traits can best be investigated in hybrid progeny. Studies of F_1 and F_2 hybrids can help to indicate the degree of complexity of polygenic traits such as skin color, hair form, body proportions, and the like. Such a characteristic as the tight spiral-tufts of Bushmen and Hottentot cannot be analyzed genetically in Bushmen or Hottentot, all of whom have it, or in Europeans who lack it. But in various Hottentot-Boer "crosses," the genetics of spiral-tuft hair form can best be tackled.

Forty years ago Caroline Bond Day collected photographs, hair samples, and pedigrees of Negro-white families. Her work helped to indicate the genetic complexity of hair form and to show that skin pigmentation was controlled by multiple genes, involving at least three loci. Studies on (aboriginal) Australian-European crosses and Asiatic-Australian crosses have further illuminated the phenomenon of graded dominance, with a particular gene acting as a dominant in one type of crossing and as a recessive in another type of crossing. Human hybrids serve a useful purpose in the analysis of many genetic traits and make up in part for our inability to institute experimental matings of the kind useful in plant and animal genetics.

Hybrid populations also afford the possibility of searching for linkage, something far less practical in old-established groups where linkage has been disrupted by crossing-over of chromosomal parts. The geneticist David Rife has conducted studies of this kind in East African populations of known and recent hybrid origin.

Finally, hybrid populations afford the possibility of calculating the degree of admixture, a useful accomplishment since historical sources are rarely quantitative. Available evidence, as investigated by D. F. Roberts and others, gives approximately 30 per cent of "European" genes to the American Colored population.

However, and contrary to popular opinion, the American Colored population contains few Amerindian genes, as Bentley Glass has demonstrated. Thus, the myth of considerable Amerindian admixture is exploded. Clearly such studies as those by Roberts or Glass prove the value of investigating geographical race hybrids (see also Fig. 22).

EUROPEAN GENES IN THE AMERICAN NEGRO

Estimating the amount of mixture (M) in a hybrid population depends upon adequate samples, not only of the hybrid population itself, but also of both parental populations. It also depends on good data, preferably for a gene that is rare in one parental group and moderate or high in the other.

Recently, Reed (1969) has reinvestigated mixture in the American Negro, using the Fy^a gene (see Chapter IV). Fy^a is rare in Africa, absent entirely in Liberia, Upper Volta, and Dahomy, and the frequency is not over 0.02 overall in the original slave territories—Liberia to the Congo. On the other hand the frequency of Fy^a is 0.42 in Southern Whites. So Fy^a is a perfect gene to test mixture (M) into the American Negro.

Taking Fy^a frequencies in American Negroes, Northern and Southern, gene frequencies are expectably lower in South Carolina and Georgia, and expectably higher in New York, California, and Michigan. From these values, Reed estimates mixture (M) and its standard error (S.E.) in American Negroes as follows:

	M	S.E.
South Carolina	0.04	± 0.01
Georgia	0.11	± 0.02
New York City	0.19	± 0.03
Oakland, Calif.	0.22	± 0.01
Detroit, Mich.	0.26	± 0.03

These new figures show the advantages of continuing research, bibliographic, historical, serological, and mathematical. They also show the need for numbers, so that estimates of Fy^a, or admixture (M) or any other parameter can have maximum reliability. Finally, they show that Northern Negroes should have appreciable frequencies of such genetic diseases as PKU, far more so than in Negroes from the American South.

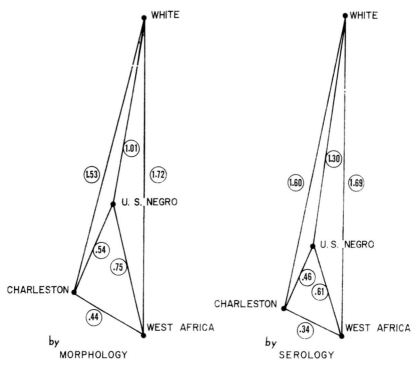

Fig. 22. Comparative "distance" between parental and hybrid populations, redrawn from Pollitzer, 1958. Sex-linkage may account for the somewhat different values obtained from morphological traits *(left)* and serological traits *(right)*.

HYBRIDIZATION, ADVANTAGES AND DISADVANTAGES

In the last century race mixture was viewed as totally bad, with dire consequences visited upon the hybrid progeny. Plant geneticists, however, discovered the phenomenon of hybrid vigor, thus pointing to a possible advantage of hybridization though such has by no means been conclusively demonstrated in man. What can we say now about the advantages and disadvantages of hybridization, or race-crossing in *Homo sapiens?*

Taking the long view and centering our attention on the population, hybridization may be considered as advantageous. By increasing genetic variability, there is a greater range of genotypes to work from, a greater likelihood of adaptive genotypes and far better prospects for long-term survival. In the long run, the more different genes the better, and race-crossing enhances genetic diversity. A hybrid race has superior long-range prospects.

The short-range view, however, centering attention upon individuals rather than the population, can be somewhat different. If a population is optimally adapted to the environment, the introduction of new genes will lower average individual fitness until the balance is restored by natural selection. But this answer itself needs qualification and emendation, as shown in the following example.

Take an East African population constantly beset by malaria and with a high incidence of the sickling gene. This population is optimally adapted to its circumstances. Admixture with non-sickling peoples would result in decreased average fitness, until such time as the balance is restored by selection. For this particular example, admixture is bad for the *individuals* concerned.

If we move this African population (or control malaria with DDT, ditch drainage, and quinine) the situation may become quite different. The "hybrids" with a lower incidence of the sickling disease would exhibit increased fitness, relative to the original population.

So the "fitness" of hybrids depends very much upon circumstances. Given a population highly adapted to particular circumstances, and an intrusive population not so adapted, the hybrids would be less fit than one parental group (though more than the second). Change the circumstances and the hybrids may be superior in fitness to the first group but not the second. In a third set of circumstances hybrid fitness may be superior to both parental groups.

GENETIC ADVANTAGES OF OUT-MARRIAGE

Inbreeding is notably disadvantageous where recessive genes are concerned. The progeny of cousins are especially susceptible to such genetically determined recessive diseases as Morquio's syndrome, PKU, amaurotic familial idiocy (A.F.I.), albinism, and many disorders of lipid metabolism. In-group marriage is also disadvantageous, from exactly the same point of view, where gene frequencies for these and other recessive disorders are initially high.

Out-group marriage would reduce the frequency of Tay-Sachs disease, which occurs in 1 out of 6,000 Jewish births as against 1 in 500,000 non-Jewish births in the U.S.A. Out-group marriage would surely reduce the frequency of PKU, which occurs in 1 in 10,000 newborns of European origin as against 1 in 100,000 Japanese and one in 250,000 American Negro live births (cf. Ch. VII). Out-marriage would reduce the frequency of homozygotes for sickle-cell disease, G6PDD, and many other hemoglobin and red-cell enzyme abnormalities.

While out-group marriage or out-marriage would reduce the disease frequency for a vast number of genetically determined conditions from albinism to Wilson's disease (a disorder of copper metabolism) general out-marriage, race mixture, or hybridization would also *increase* the probabilities of Rh incompatibility (with European–non-European matings), MNS-U incompatibilities, and maternal-foetal incompatibilities involving the ABO system.

Furthermore, genetic advantages and disadvantages of out-marriage would depend upon the groups involved, the geographical and ecological locale, and a great variety of social and cultural situations. Out-marriage for smaller isolates in the U.S.A. could be viewed as advantageous, but to be weighed against in-group traditions that produce a high proportion of socially useful citizens. Still untested is the possibility of maternal-foetal dispro-portions, which remains theoretical; and not to be ignored is the question of social acceptance. In the U.S.A., Japanese-American "hybrids" have high social acceptance, but in Japan this is at present unfortunately far from true.

SUMMARY

Race mixture, involving distinct gene-pools, is an old human accomplishment, increasing genetic diversity, producing new adaptive peaks, and making for more rapid evolutionary change.

Depending upon circumstances, individual fitness may be higher or lower, but population fitness increases. Since gene-flow in modern times has often been unidirectional, one population may be changed and the other not.

In extreme cases, all Y chromosomes will then come from one group and the majority of the X chromosomes from another, in which case males and females will not be equally "distant" from the two parental populations for some generations.

SUGGESTED READINGS

Day, C. B.: *A Study of Some Negro-White Families in the United States.* Cambridge, Peabody Museum, 1932.

*Glass, B.: On the unlikelihood of significant admixture of genes from The North American Indians in the present composition of the Negroes of the United States. *Am. J. Human Genet.*, 7:368-385, 1955.

Pollitzer, W.S.: The Negroes of Charleston (S. C.), a study of hemoglobin types, serology and morphology. *Am. J. Phys. Anthropol.*, N.S. 16:241-263, 1958.

Reed, T.E.: Caucasian genes in American Negroes. *Science, 165:*762-768, 1969.

*Roberts, D. F.: The dynamics of racial intermixture in the American Negro—some anthropological considerations. *Am. J. Human Genet.,* 7:361-367, 1955.

Shapiro, H. L.: *Descendants of the Mutineers of the Bounty.* Honolulu, Memoirs of the Bernice P. Bishop Museum, 1929, vol. 9.

Shapiro, H. L.: Race mixture. In *The Race Question in Modern Science.* New York, Morrow, 1956.

Stuckert, R. P.: African ancestry of the white American population. *Ohio J. Sci., 58:*155-160, 1958.

---

*Reprinted in *Readings on Race.*

X

RACE, BEHAVIOR AND INTELLIGENCE

RACE AND TEMPERAMENT

A CENTURY AGO most thoughtful and learned individuals firmly believed in racial differences in temperament. The stereotypes of the past century, sometimes still reiterated as fact, painted vastly different natures for the various geographical races. Asiatics were pictured as sly, mysterious, and inscrutable, and Africans were described as childlike and improvident. American Indians, with some exceptions, were portrayed as stolid, stoical, and humorless. The relationship between geographical race and temperament, from a 19th century European view, may be summarized by one quotation: "Black men are ruled by passion, yellow men are bound by custom, while white men are governed by law."

Even within geographical races, inborn differences in temperament were accepted as fact. It is part of our literary heritage to speak of melancholy Danes, musical Italians, and volatile Frenchmen. Various nations have been accused (by various other nations) as being humorless. Undesirable characteristics have been attributed by one group to the other. The Englishman speaks of "taking French leave," while the French equivalent is to "take English leave."

To some extent, these stereotypes were based on inadequate observations and were due to unfamiliarity with language and gesture. It is difficult to interpret the facial expressions of nationals from another country and still more difficult to operate in a totally different culture. At the same time some stereotypes are factual. Italians do gesticulate. Germans do eat wurst. And the Sioux Indians were notably inhospitable to General George Custer. Such stereotypes, however, neglect to distinguish learned behavior from inherent nature; they do not distinguish being

Chinese from speaking Mandarin, nor a hundred generations of trading experience from inherited mercantile ability.

It is, moreover, vastly interesting to see how stereotypes change with time. The noble and restrained Romans became the voluble and musical Italians without major genetic change. The patriarchal Hebrews became the peddlers and merchants despite little accretion of outside genes. The woad-painted, skin-draped barbarians near Londinium, of Augustus' time, became the chief carriers of western culture two millennia later. The same English yeoman stock gave rise to the nasal Yankees, the elegant Virginians, the backwoods Appalachians, and the Texans.

Clearly, the outstanding character traits that do distinguish groups are culturally determined and culturally formed. Associations between occupation and nationality melt like wax with changes in social mobility, with improved education, and with altered economic status. Predilections toward criminality, initially characteristic of each immigrant group into the United States, disappear with succeeding generations. Even the pattern of criminal proclivity, characteristically different in various national groups when they first arrive, rapidly readjusts to the general norm as is clearly evident in the table on this page. Given such data, claims for true racial differences in criminal preferences rapidly dissipate.

CONVICTION RATES FOR SPECIFIED CRIMES*

Offense	Irish Immigrants	Second Generation	Native "White"
Homicide	2.3	1.0	0.5
Rape	0.0	0.3	0.7
Gambling	1.2	2.7	3.6

*From Sutherland, E. H., and Creasey, D. R.: *Prinicples of Criminology*. Philadelphia, J. B. Lippincott, 1955.

So far, there is no evidence for racial differences in character and temperament other than those due to cultural conditioning. The same may be said for behavior in general. With respect to psychotic behavior, however, there may well be some differences. Some of the differences noted between Italian and Irish psychiatric patients may have a genic background. Differences in adrenochrome production, in serotonin levels in the brain, even in the central nervous system, may explain apparent racial differences in the predisposition to particular psychiatric disorders. Such differences, however, have not been demonstrated on a racial basis, holding the way of life constant.

Still, the most profitable area for investigation would seem to lie in the autonomic nervous system. There are clear-cut, reproducible individual differences in autonomic response specificity. Individuals exhibit marked and consistent responses to various kinds of stress. Racial differences in gene-determined response patterns are very likely, especially when one considers the adaptive nature some of these response patterns must hold in nature. Racial differences in behavior therefore may fall to the psychophysiologist to discover and will not encompass most areas of social behavior.

RACE AND INTELLIGENCE

Much as racial differences in temperament were firmly credited in the century now past, marked hereditary and racial differences in intellectual capacity were also accepted as self-evident truths. Long before Binet's measurements of intellectual accomplishment were published in 1905, literate and technologically advanced Europeans held low opinions of the intelligence of illiterate and technologically simple "natives." What the natives thought of the Europeans unfortunately is not on record.

Intelligence tests, originally developed and used as guides for the grade-placement of school children, at first provided powerful support for the assumption of racial differences in intellectual capacity. Native-born Americans ranked highest. Immigrant children from northwestern Europe came next. At the bottom of the list were American Negro children. Since Binet's test demanded reading skills, and many of the Negroes were largely illiterate, a substantial proportion were rated in the dull-normal, dull, borderline, and subnormal categories.

More recent studies have shown that "intelligence" as earlier measured is not a constant, that it is susceptible to change even in adults, that it is a function of the environment and of opportunity, and that it can be inhibited by malnutrition and disease. When it is measured in terms of vocabulary, mathematical ability, reasoning skills, and ability to express abstractions, motivated children of urban, bookish, verbal families test out the best, while the children of poor families, broken families, families with limited vocabularies, and families without books show the lowest I.Q. scores.

Today, it is quite clear that intelligence tests, such as the Stanford revision of Binet's, or the Wechsler-Bellevue, or the Otis, do not primarily measure inherent gene-determined potentialities. Intelligence tests are still validated against schol performance; they measure a "book" kind of proficiency. Such tests do not purport to measure many of the skills and abilities that the term intelligence commonly suggests. Intelligence tests, moreover, are never culture-free. They measure in relation to a particular cultural background, placing premiums on language skills, urban living, and acquired knowledge, thus down-rating rural, non-verbal or immigrant children or adults. I.Q. test scores neatly reflect the level of motivation and (except at the extremes) not inherent ability.

Quite obviously it is impractical to get meaningful comparative intelligence scores for many preliterate people. Even the culture-free test is a misnomer, being a culture-constant test, or else an impossibility. Comparing or equating test scores for a Chinese peasant boy from Langsai and a merchant's son from London introduces extraordinary problems. Only where education, opportunity, and the way of life are uniform across racial barriers can meaningful comparisons be made. Possibly comparative testing can be accomplished in Hawaii. Possibly multi-racial orphanages may yield the critical data, though institutional conditions rarely afford the child an adequate opportunity to develop the skills most highly rated on the tests.

Racial differences in measured intelligence thus remain neither proven nor disproved. There are differences, but like stature, they do not necessarily indicate the maximum level of capacity in the absence of standard or controlled conditions. To the confirmed believer in racial differences in intelligence, we can simply say that the more nearly two groups are matched in educational level, family background, opportunity, and security, the closer they agree on averaged I.Q. scores. To the dedicated equalitarian, the believer in no race differenecs, the disparate levels in the currently best-matched Negro-white comparisons stand to be refuted.

As a matter of opinion, backed by some personal experience with mental test data, one may question whether major racial differences in working intelligence could have arisen, except in remote areas, during the millennia of human evolution. For most of man's million-year existence, the way of life of one group strongly resembled the life-way of another. Life in Paleolithic England and Stone-Age Tanganyika were much alike. With a salubrious climate there arose population pressure and man organized to outsmart man. In less equable climes man organized to counter nature. One may question whether it took more brains to succeed in Neolithic Ireland or in the Indus Valley in the New Stone Age.

Europe, moreover, was not always the center of technological advancement, having attained that status rather late in human affairs (and even now the baton is passing). Europeans, in fact, did not compete with each other on a purely intellectual basis until rather recently, but still only a fraction of a per cent later than Egyptians or Mesopotamians. Besides, one may well wonder whether it takes more "intelligence" to survive in Kansas City than in the Kalahari. Only if there were long-continued differential selection for intelligence in some areas, and not in others, could we expect true racial differences in intelligence to exist.

Yet, it would be a mistake to ignore intelligence completely in considering either race or race differences. Different skills have had adaptive value in different areas and in some cases over a respectable number of generations. Eskimo mechanical genius stands out as one example, and mechanical skill appears to be one of the "special" abilities. The exquisite form-color sense possessed by many peoples from Japan to Thailand to Burma may well represent a second example of special skill differentially distributed with respect to race.

A very reasonable guess is that races are comparable in the

sum and total of what we call "intelligence," but differ in many interesting details. As with the autonomic response patterns that so neatly differentiate one individual from the other, race differences may exist in form-discrimination, color-sense, tonal-memory, mechanical reasoning, abstract reasoning, and other special (rather than general) aspects of intelligence. This supposition, moreover, is directly susceptible to testing.

RACE, POPULATION AND INTELLECTUALLY HANDICAPPING CONDITIONS

Apart from the argument, about race and intelligence, there is the highly important problem of intellectually handicapping conditions in different population groups. Populations may differ in the proportion of impaired individuals on a nutritional basis, due to iodine deficiency, B-vitamin deficiency or quality protein deficiencies in critical periods of development. They may differ simply because of differences in obstetric care and neonatal anoxia. They may differ because of prenatal exposure to rubella or postnatal exposure to rubeola. Populations may differ in the incidence of genetically determined enzyme defects—PKU, maple-sugar urine disease, and other abnormalities of amino acid metabolism. They do differ, genetically, in the incidence of microcephaly, bird-headed dwarfs, Carpenter's syndrome, and in the neurological disorders and dysautonomias described earlier. In some cases, one can even demonstrate a founder effect for a specific form of intellectual handicap, originating in Vilna or in Paris.

Writing in the *Proceedings of the 8th Congress of Anthropological and Ethnological Sciences* (1968, 247-248), D. Carleton Gajdusek describes genetic and environmental factors which may influence the neurological endowment of diverse human groups. He points out how exposures to specific toxins may vary from one culture to another (a reference, surely, to cycad toxicity in the Pacific), the role of inbreeding, and even population differences in the extent of head injuries.

Continuing the quotation from Gajdusek, he writes as follows:

> Interesting, in our work in Oceania we have already encountered whole population groups wherein the problem of minimal to moderate

brain dysfunction of a high portion of the population is flagrantly evident.

1) The Kup population near Kerowahgi in the Central Highlands of New Guinea where postencephalitic brain injuries of widely varying degree of severity are clearly diagnosable in a high percentage of the children;

2) The population of the whole western portion of the Highlands of West New Guinea from the western headwaters of the Ruffaer River westward through to the borders of the Kapaukua population around the Wisselmeeren, where an enormous problem of CNS defect associated with endemic goiterous cretinism affects the majority of the population, involving all members of several linguistic groups such as the Dauwa, Moni, and Uhunduni and many of the Western Dani;

3) Several small coral island and atoll populations of Micronesia wherein evident moderate intellectual impairment—true familial feeble-mindedness—affects a high percentage of the population.

All these forms of brain damage are superimposed upon the genetically determined structure of the brain.

HANDICAPPING DEFECTS OF CHROMOSOMAL ORIGIN

While the frequency of specific genetically determined, intellectually handicapping defects does differ from race to race, as explained above, those of chromosomal origin apparently do not. Down's syndrome (formerly called "mongolism"), usually due to an extra G-group chromosome, has no racial bias. Similarly, abnormalities in the number of sex chromosomes, commonly associated with mental retardation, are equally frequent in Northwest Europe, the United States, Central America, India, and Africa (Van Den Berghe, 1970). XXY and XYY males and XXX and XO females so far appear to be equally common the world around.

SUMMARY

Racial differences in gesture, speech, emotionality, and way of life clearly exist, but these have proven to be largely differences acquired in the social matrix. With migration, acculturation, or even the simple passage of time, racial "characteristics" change immensely as in the case of the rude and crude woad-painted natives of colonial Britain. While no racial differences in temperament, behavior or intellectual capacity have been firmly established as gene-determined, and while such complexes as overall behavior or overall intelligence may not differ from race to race, there is every likelihood that components of behavior may be gene-determined, with differences in frequency from population to population. Here attention may be directed to the patterns of autonomic response to stress, to differential skills and abilities, and to susceptibility to emotional disorders. Races may also differ in early postnatal behavior as well (Freedman and Freedman, 1969), as they do in early postnatal ossification.

SUGGESTED READINGS

Anastasi, A.: *Differential Psychology*. New York, Macmillan, 1958.

Anastasi, A.: Heredity and psychological trait. In Gedda, L. (Ed.) : *De Genetica Medica*. Rome, Gregor Mendel Institute, 1962, Vol. II.

Eels, K., Davis, A., Havighurst, R. J., Herrick, V. E., and Tyler, R. W.: *Intelligence and Cultural Differences*. Chicago, University of Chicago Press, 1951.

Freedman, D. G., and Freedman, N. C.: Behavioural differences between Chinese-Americans and European-American newborns. *Nature, 224:*1221, 1969.

Klineberg, O.: *Race Differences*. New York, Harper and Bros., 1935.

Kagan, J., and Moss, H.: Parental correlates of child's I.Q. and height. *Child Develop., 30:*325-332, 1959.

Lacey, J. I., and Lacey, B. C.: Verification and extension of the principle of autonomic response stereotype. *Am. J. Psychol., 71:*50-73, 1958.

Moss, H., and Kagan, J.: Maternal influences on early I.Q. scores. *Psych. Reports, 4:*655-661, 1958.

The Race Question in Modern Science. UNESCO publications, New York, Morrow, 1959.

Van Den Berghe, H.: Nuclear sexing in a population of Congolese metropolitan newborns. *Science, 169:*1318-1320, 1970.

Willerman, L., Naylor, A. F., and Myrianthopoulos, N. C.: Intellectual development of children from interracial matings. *Science, 170:* 1329-1331, 1970.

XI

TAXONOMY IN MAN

$\mathbf{A}$ TAXONOMY is a listing and an accounting and an enumeration of the larger and smaller taxonomic groupings for any life form. Ultimately, a taxonomy is concerned with the species, and in a highly specialized taxonomy (as is necessary for man), with units smaller than the species.

A taxonomy is a simple attempt to describe the natural populations that actually occur. For that reason, the taxonomist tries to make his groupings conform to natural populations having finite and known breeding limits. Where these limits are not known for sure, or where a series of microgeographical races appears to exist, the taxonomist must then make use of all available data to estimate the amount of population difference. A taxonomy, after all, is an effort to describe nature, not an attempt to dictate to her.

Naturally, as new information appears, taxonomies may need to be revised. Blood groups, haptoglobins, hemoglobins, and the serum, transferrins have helped to illuminate problems of human classification, particularly in the Western Pacific. Taxonomies must also be revised in the light of current thinking, in some cases decreasing the number of separate units by combining them, and in other cases increasing the number of taxonomic units by adding new groupings as the need becomes apparent.

The fact that human taxonomy is in the process of continuous revision is in no way a reflection upon taxonomy as a whole, upon specific human taxonomies, or upon particular human taxonomists. We know of the existence of many completely valid local races that have been formed within the last few hundred years. We know of other races that have become extinct in the same time period. We know how our expanding knowledge dictates revision of expanding thought. Indeed, it would be remarkable if classifications of man used in pre-Darwinian times could be employed totally without change today.

ARTIFICIAL KEYS TO TAXONOMY

In the attempt to simplify identification, taxonomists sometimes seize upon a few simple and obvious morphological differences. Entomologists dealing with butterflies employ the patterns of the wing veins or the morphology of the antennae as a quick way of distinguishing one group from another. Botanists make use of the parts of the flower or variations in the form of the leaf to provide a simple key to identification. Such aids constitute *artificial keys* to taxonomy. They greatly simplify the task of identification.

In dealing with man, similar artificial keys have been constructed again and again. Most familiar are keys based upon apparent skin color or upon hair form or upon head form. Other such keys to human identification have involved the ABO blood groups, the ratio of A to O and the ratio of B to A and O. As with artificial keys used in entomology or botany, these are helpful aids for use in the field, but they are not natural taxonomies; they are not based on actual breeding populations. It is necessary to distinguish between artificial keys that have particular use in identification and a natural taxonomy that deals with populations as they are seen to exist.

OBJECTIONS TO HUMAN TAXONOMIES

From time to time, objections have been raised to particular human taxonomies or particular approaches to human taxonomy. In the course of this book we have repeatedly objected to the old typological approach, involved hypothetical "types" and the inference that such types recreate actual origins. Objections may be raised, also, to the older and now obsolete attempts to view all mankind in terms of a single set of origins, involving at most a relatively few "original" groups. Whatever Ham, Shem, and Japheth meant in Biblical times, a simple trinitarian origin for man is contradicted by all observed facts today.

Another objection occasionally heard is that the taxonomists do not agree among themselves. This criticism is valid in certain cases, to be sure. However, when a human taxonomist has made use of actual population data and has stated good reasons for making his taxonomic distinctions, we may disagree with him but we cannot disagree with the decisions themselves. Where taxonomists do disagree one with the other, we find particular problem areas needed investigation, requiring additional field confirmation, and neatly indicating areas where research is particularly needed.

Another objection, occasionally heard, is that the existence of *intergrades* between different geographical races vitiates the purpose of taxonomy in man. Now integrades certainly occur. We may view the people of Ethiopia as one set of intergades and certain of the Madagascar peoples as another. But intergrades in man, like intergrades in other species, hardly defeat the purpose of taxonomy. Rather, such intergrades point up the role of taxonomy. Are the intergrades simply the products of race mixture? If so, what has kept race mixture from occurring where other geographical races meet? Or are these "intergrades" actually the product of competing directions of natural selection, producing intermediacy by removing both extremes from the population? If so, we need to know why such intermediate populations do not exist elsewhere, answers that we can obtain both by exploring the historical record and the rates of natural selection.

Intergrades, in fact, identify particular areas and problems for intensive study. One purpose of taxonomy is to pose the question why? And this question is particularly posed by intergrades.

DIFFERENCES IN APPROACH TO HUMAN TAXONOMY

In fact, it is quite impossible to avoid taxonomic assignments and taxonomic language in dealing with man. The decision to employ only geographical races of man (or "stock," or whatever) involves the decision to employ taxonomic units of a particular size or level. Nor can taxonomy be avoided by referring only to actual breeding populations, as suggested by Livingstone (1963). This decision itself represents a commitment to taxonomy, that is, it recognizes the separateness of the groups so designated. But further, it leaves totally open the taxonomic equivalents of the population so designated. Inevitably, a "non-taxonomy" includes as many implicit taxonomic assumptions as an out-and-out taxonomy!

The distinction between the Western Aleut of Attu and Atka and the Eastern Aleut of Umnak and Unalaska is a taxonomic distinction. The geographically and linguistically isolated Mayan villages that are dotted around Lake Atitlan suggest taxonomic differences, the more so when the inhibitants are compared. The use of place names does not circumvent taxonomy. Rather, it indicates that the user has taxonomic implications in mind.

Some groupings of mankind represent larger, higher taxonomic units, closer to the species. Others are smaller or "lower" taxonomic units, down to the circumscribed local breeding populations. Even when attempting to avoid taxonomy, taxonomic language and taxonomic implications are inevitable.

There are, of course, legitimate differences in approach to human taxonomy. A particular worker (such as William C. Boyd) may prefer to concern himself with geographical races of man. Or, various human taxonomists may differ in the degree of local differentiation they may care to recognize. Thus, Birdsell divides Australian aborigines into two or more distinct groupings on the basis of local, morphological, and polygenic differences. Professor Abbie, in turn, currently sees reason for only one such grouping among the aborigines of Australia. Birdsell and Abbie quite agree that there are local differences; they disagree only on the magnitude and the duration of the reproductive barriers these differences presently suggest.

Now the American Indians clearly and obviously share much in common with the peoples of mainland Asia from whom they must be ultimately derived. Yet the American Indians differ also, each from the other and group by group, from the peoples of mainland Asia. The magnitude of the differences, morphological, serological, and biochemical, the apparent time depth (10,000 to 40,000 years) seems sufficient to the writer to distinguish the American Indians and Asiatics as separate geographical races.

But there are other workers who view Asiatics and Amerindians as having so much in common as to place both in a single, polytypic geographical race. To take a specific example, do the cerumen types "dry" and "wet" in Seminole Indians place them in the Asiatic ("Mongoloid") category, or does the cerumen polymorphism together with the virtual absence of B and the lack of the MN polymorphism make the Native Americans a separate taxonomic unit?

Some workers have tended to view the Bushmen and Hottentots as a "Capoid" Geographical Race, related to but separate from the African Geographical Race in general (Coon, 1962). Indeed, there is historical evidence for a considerable period of separation between the smaller, more slender, and lighter-skinned peoples of the Cape region and those from Equatorial Africa. However, reveiwing the serological data, the haptoglobins, and the abnormal hemoglobins, it does not appear to the writer that the Bushmen-Hottentots constitute a valid geographical race. Indeed, their short stature and skinny shanks tend to change as they become marginal farm workers with an assured caloric supply. Still, the amount of difference between the "Capoid" and the other Africans remains a point of discussion, a problem to be solved.

Such differences in taxonomic opinion are both legitimate and salutary. They point out problem areas that need resolution. Areas of agreement, on the other hand, may reflect problems long settled, or they may reflect a virtual lack of information.

THE PURPOSE OF HUMAN TAXONOMY

One purpose of human taxonomy is both immediate and self-evident. It is to encompass man as we know him, to put the groups of man in place and in some sort of contemporary order. It is to give a true common language and full common meaning to the terms we prefer to use. When you use the term "Polynesians" and I use the term "Polynesians," and he uses the term "Polynesians," it is important to know that we all refer to, and more or less agree upon, the same island groups with identical geographical boundaries.

Taxonomy and taxonomic assignments inevitably imply some sort of history. Separate groups have presumably had separate origins and separate histories. And geographical races that we put next to each other on a taxonomy, presumably have (or have had) a communality of early origins but later divergences. No matter how religiously we may try to avoid it, taxonomy inevitably implies phylogeny. To quote Simpson (1963) :

> Phylogeny is the appropriate theoretical background for taxonomy . . . Important disagreement persists only as to the desirable or practicable relationship between phylogeny and classification, and especially whether phylogeny can and should provide criteria for classification, or can and should play its toxonomic role only in interpreting classifications based on other criteria.

The mere existence of a race has historical, phylogenetic, and evolutionary implications of its own. The fact that a race exists at all immediately raises the question, why? Why are the Australians different from the New Guineans in blood group B and other serological traits? One wonders how ancient these differences are. Do Australian aborigines and natives of New Guinea differ for 5,000 years back, or 50,000 years, or perhaps even 500,-000 years? Do their differences antedate their present locations or are current differences on-the-spot examples of local directions of evolutionary change? The fact that a race appears in a taxonomy raises the evolutionary question, why? the geographical question, where? and the historical question, when?

True enough, a taxonomy, whether human or otherwise, is a collection of pigeonholes. In true Victorian fashion, it does picture races known and others still to be heard from. But any taxonomy asks questions of its own. It asks the student of climatic adaptation and geographical medicine to answer the question, why? It asks the historical and archaeological anthropologist to consider the question, where? and it forces the paleo-anthropologist and the paleontologist to answer the question, when? Besides communication, there are the purposes of any taxonomy; these are the purposes of taxonomy in man.

HUMAN TAXONOMY AND FOSSIL MAN

Because we are in the fortunate position of being able to study natural human populations, breeding and interbreeding and spreading today, we can extend our taxonomic experience backward to the study of fossil man. We know exactly how large the differences between particular local races can be. We are able to compare long-isolated geographical races of living man. From such comparisons of smaller and larger taxonomic units now, we are in a better position to do a better job of classifying *sapiens* and pre-*sapiens* forms of *Homo*.

Fossil categories are, as Mayr (1950) so neatly observes, inferences as to natural categories that once existed. When we say now that two fossil groupings, for example Sinanthropus and Pithecanthropus, are at most *geographical* races of *Homo*, we do so knowing the extent to which geographical races of man can differ now. When we say that the Neanderthals and their various groups were at most variants of a single geographical race of *Homo sapiens,* we necessarily base our judgment on the extent to which geographical races may be observed to differ today.

Taxonomy of fossil hominids rests upon our actual knowledge of contemporary human populations. The taxonomic assignments we make for living man inevitably serve as models for fossil *taxa*. Two fossil groupings may be considered as co-specific if they differ no more than geographical races of mankind do now. Two fossil specimens may be considered as co-racial if they differ no more than individuals from a single breeding population do now.

In this way, knowing the populations of modern man that exist and the taxonomic positions we give them, we can better elucidate taxonomic problems in fossil man, whose breeding habits we can at best infer. Thus it is that taxonomy, besides presenting present problems, represents one use of the present to delineate the evolutionary past.

SUMMARY

A taxonomy is a listing of higher and lower taxonomic units, corresponding, as nearly as is possible, to biological populations and revised, as the need arises, to conform with new data and initial information as they become available. At the very least, taxonomy is essential to scientific communication. Taxonomy provides a communality of names and labels for all to use. Taxonomy is a device through which scientists make sure that they are referring to the same natural groupings in making comparisons. But the ultimate purpose of a taxonomy goes beyond communication. With its listing of separate local races and distinct geographical races, a taxonomy asks why the units exist. It asks how they have come to differ each from the other. It asks when the differences came about. And it asks where the differentiation actually occurred.

A taxonomy points out groupings that have had separate evolutionary histories and imposes the basic evolutionary questions: where, when, how, and why?

SUGGESTED READINGS

*Garn, S. M.: Taxonomy in recent and fossil man. In Garn, S. M. (Ed.) : *Readings on Race.* Springfield, Thomas, 1968, pp. 307-312.

Livingstone, F. B.: Comment on Newman's paper "Geographic and Microgeographic Races." *Current Anthropol., 4:*199-200, 1963.

Mayr, E., *Animal Species and Evolution.* Cambridge, The Belknap Press of Harvard University, 1963.

Mayr, E.: Taxonomic categories in fossil hominids. *Cold Spring Harbor Symposia on Quantitative Biology, 15:*109-118, Cold Spring Harbor, The Biological Laboratory, 1950.

Newman, M.: Geographic and microgeographic races. *Current Anthropol., 4:*189-192, 1963.

Rensch, B.: *Evolution Above the Species Level.* Columbia Biological Series XIX. New York, Columbia University Press, 1960.

Simpson, G. G.: *Principles of Animal Taxonomy.* Columbia Biological Series XX. New York, Columbia University Press, 1961.

Simpson, G. G.: The meaning of taxonomic statements. In Washburn, S. L. (Ed.) : *Classification and Human Evolution, 37:*1-31, Chicago, Aldine Publishing Company, 1963.

Washburn, S. L.: The study of race. *Am. Anthropol., 65:*521-531, 1963.

*Johnston, F. E.: Racial taxonomies from an evolutionary perspective, *Am. Anthropol., 66:*822-827, 1964.

XII

A TAXONOMY FOR MAN

For man, that is, for all of living man, there is but one extant species which Linnaeus hopefully termed *sapiens*. All men now are the same sort of animal. All men now inhibit the same adaptive plateau. All mankind can interbreed, given the chance, and in fact all mankind usually does. It is likely that pre-*sapiens, erectus* hominids, were eliminated less by warfare or by superior cunning than by the pervasive human preoccupation with exchanging genes.

Thus it is that mankind consists of but one species now. Despite time and reproductive isolation, neither have been sufficient to bring about new species in our genus since *sapiens* man became the dominant life form. Yet, in geographically separate areas of the world, with oceans or deserts or mountain groups limiting gene flow, collections of human geographical races ultimately developed. Some of these geographical races are sufficiently different and sufficiently distinct to approach valid subspecies. Other and contiguous geographical races evidence much less differentiation, with intergrades along the geographical borders where they now meet.

THE NUMBER OF GEOGRAPHICAL RACES

Taken together, the number of geographical races of living man is by no means large. If we ignore a few populations such as the Ainu that possibly represent the last survivors of once-larger geographical groupings, there are surely not more than nine or ten geographical races of mankind today. Nor, for that matter, are there many less. It is therefore possible to describe these geographical races, to set forth the distinguishing characteristics as they have developed over time and to give the reasons for the taxonomic assignments, all within a single chapter.

However, geographical races are not breeding populations. They are collections of breeding populations, all inhabiting geographically defined areas. Within a geographical race, overall resemblances are ordinarily greater than they are between them, simply because gene-exchange has been more intensive within geographical races and because geographical races share many selective factors in common. Though the sickle-cell gene appears elsewhere and is not completely "African," still it is in Africa that this gene is most frequent (cf. Singer, 1962). However, in particular genetically determined traits, resemblances may exist across geographical races, either because of earlier common ancestry (as we infer for β-AIB in Asia and America) or because of common selective factors. Thus, the isogenic "islands" of non-tasters in Asia, Africa, India, and Europe are presumably without communality of origins. And in numerous parts of the world, directions of malarial selection have favored a variety of abnormal hemoglobins and a variety of enzymatic adaptations quite independently, as Blumberg (1963) has shown.

Clearly, geographical races are not genetically uniform units, nor would they be expected to be. Selective factors are never uniform within any large geographical area or within any continent. Climatic selection, nutritional selection, and disease selection have affected each separate breeding population in different ways. Lowlanders have more access to products of the sea and are less likely to be protein-deficient than are highlanders. Migration, genetic drift, and the "bottleneck effect" have all affected the genetic makeup of populations within a geographical race. So it is useless to question the "purity" of those East Africans who are less than fully dark, or of those Asiatics who are less than the hypothetical Mongoloid extreme. The fact that local races within every geographical area do differ from each other is the subject for investigation, one of the major reasons for the continuing study of race in man. Local differentiation is not a failure of taxonomy; it is one of the problems posed by taxonomy.

There are nine geographical races that we are about to describe. They currently fit the criteria of being mutually exclusive (Garn, 1963). In the light of present evidence, one could not now be part of another, though contiguous geographical races necessarily resemble each other more than do those spatially more apart. These nine (or ten) geographical races of man exist. They correspond reasonably to major geographical barriers to reproduction as we know them now. And these geographical races pose all of the major evolutionary problems mentioned in the last chapter on taxonomy. We want to know when they came about, why they came about and how they came to be different. But, by their very geographic location they answer the question, where?

THE ANTIQUITY OF GEOGRAPHICAL RACES

How ancient are the present geographical races of mankind: 5,000 years, 50,000 years, or 500,000 years? Clearly, there were people in Asia, Africa, and Europe half a million years ago and more. Clearly, human differentiation then existing was at least equivalent to geographical races now. Presumably, some of the Pleistocene genes were transmitted to the present inhabitants in these same geographical areas. It is reasonable to believe that contemporary Asiatics share more genes in common with the Pleistocene inhabitants of Asia than they do with the Pleistocene inhabitants of Africa. In this much, Crenshaw (1964) agrees with Professor C. S. Coon (1962).

But races do not remain constant. They change. Natural selection or directed genetic change and nondirected sources of genetic change are continually at work. Some local populations expand tremendously and others die out. Some populations change their genetic makeup rapidly, others at a slower pace. It is unlikely that any geographical race today closely resembles the collection of races in the same geographical area 500,000 or 50,-000 or in some cases even 5,000 years ago.

How old are particular geographical races? In one sense, geographical races are as old as geographical differentiation within the successional species *Homo erectus* and *Homo sapiens*. But in another and much more biological sense, geographical races are continually changing to the point that all geographical races are equally young. We know that present frequencies of the sickle-cell gene in Africa are relatively recent. We know that they are changing now. We know that the Northwest Europeans were relatively few in number 2,000 years ago, yet today they comprise the largest subgrouping of the European geographical race. If the component populations of geographical races are subject to continuing change, if the genetic makeup changes over time, do geographical races remain the same? Does one geographical race actually have greater "antiquity" than another?

A LISTING OF GEOGRAPHICAL RACES

1. The Amerindian Geographical Race (the "aboriginal" American Indians) consists of a large number of local populations ranging from Alaska to Labrador and southward to the tip of South America (see map). Often marginal and food gatherers

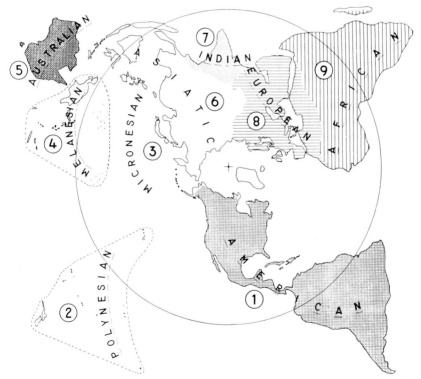

Fig. 23. Polar-projection map of the world showing the approximate limits of the geographical races described in the text. This spread-out view shows that large areas of ocean have contributed to reproductive isolation while continguous land masses allow for easier gene-flow.

for the most part, individual Ameriandian populations were generally small and isolated in pre-Columbian times, thus maximizing the chance for genetic diversity. But in the highland areas of Middle and South America, intensive maize agriculture allowed population expansion and more frequent gene interchange that reduced local differentiation. A similar local uniformization presumably occurred in the American Southwest.

Amerindians are set off from Asiatics by the absence of blood group B, extraordinarily low values of N, and no r at all. They share, with Asiatics, β-AIB high-excretors, the Diego-positive gene (Di^a), the dry-earwax type, and at least one rare hemoglobin variant (cf. *Am. J. Phys. Anthropol., 30:*389-392, 1969). They are clearly of Asia, from Asia, but with 3,000 to 25,000 years of separation. Paradoxically, Central American and South American Indians have a higher frequency of "Asian" genes.

Morphologically , Amerindians exhibit a high frequency of shovel-shaped teeth often developed to a remarkable extent (see Carbonell, 1963), suture bones (Fig. 24), etc. Head hair is generally coarse and straight. Body, facial and axillary hair are always sparse. Male pattern balding and acne are both rare.

Once, local differentiation in the Americas was attributed to successive "waves" of migrations. Today, such diversity is generally accepted as the result of natural selection acting on generally small population isolates (Newman, 1953), some of whom may have a respectable antiquity of as much as 20,000 years, as shown by radiocarbon dating.

2. The Polynesian Geographical Race occupies a vast territory in the Pacific, ranging from New Zealand to Hawaii and Easter (Pascua) Island. Many now uninhabited islands of the Pacific bear relics of these hardy, seafaring folk, some of whom were still on their eastward migration at the time of Captain Cook's voyages.

Polynesian polymorphism is marked for hair form, skin color, nose form, and body build. In years past, a tri-hybrid explanation was given as the most likely explanation. But we know now that the Polynesians are low in B, rather high in blood group N, and only moderately high in the Duffy factor (Fy^a). Thus, the Polynesians are more or less typically "Pacific," quite unlike mainland

Fig. 24. Suture bones or "Wormian bones" on the skull of a New York State Indian, (coutesy of the New York State Museum, see Bennett, *Am. J. Phys. Anthrop.*, 23:255-260). According to Keith Hertzog, such accessory centers are part of a development field that includes other sutural areas.

Asia and certainly quite un-European (no *r*, no A₂, etc.). So while linguistic evidence may indicate ultimate Asian origins, it is apparent that natural selection has favored blood group N, it has favored A over B, and it has eliminated several of the Rh alleles, thus making the polytypic Polynesians what they are today.

3. The Micronesian Geographical Race, as the name obviously implies, occupies a series of tiny islands in the Pacific. The members are dark-skinned, generally small, and they have the wavy to helical hair frequently referred to as "frizzed" in the older accounts.

Serologically, the Micronesians are much like the Polynesians except for respectably higher frequencies of B. Blood group A is rather common, with a gene frequency in excess of 0.5. N generally exceeds M. Largely Duffy-positive (Fy^a) and nearly Diego-negative, the peoples of Micronesia are set off both from Polynesia and from Australia. They have far too much blood group B for either. Yet the data on Diego and β-AIB shut them off genetically from the Asian mainland as well.

This morphological and serological picture is completely consistent with directions of local selection in such islands as Ulithi, Palau, Yap, and the Marshall and Gilbert Islands. It suggests that the Pacific area has a communality of selective factors.

4. The Melanesian-Papuan Geographical Race, practically isolated until World War II, exemplifies the old problem of using morphological similarities alone to prove "origins." With dark skins and hair that curls, twists and frizzes, the Melanesians (from the Greek word *melas* meaning "black") were once viewed as Africans way out of place. We realize now that all dark skins need not have a common origin. Serologically the Melanesians are most un-African. Dentally they are un-African, too.

But New Guinea, New Britain, and the Solomons contain hundreds of isolated linguistic and cultural groups, some coastal and some living at altitudes well over 5,000 feet. In the lower, more malarial areas of New Guinea, the G6PD deficiency is not uncommon, with gene frequencies up to 0.3. At higher altitudes, expectably, this enzymatic polymorphism is rarer (see suggested readings).

Melanesians have blood group B, unlike the Australians, S (in the MN-S series), and high levels of blood group N. As described earlier in this book, they have Kuru, in at least one area, they have the thalassemia gene, and they are subject to constant selection by a vast number of virulent viral diseases.

Fig. 25. Melanesians of New Guinea. Despite some R_0 genes, the high frequency of N and Fy^a place these highly variable, large-toothed people, square in the Pacific area genetically, while G6PDD conforms to a Pacific locus of malaria selection.

Melanesians, Papuans, and New Guineans have many elements of similarity to Australian aborigines, particularly in the south, where they are nearly contiguous. Common origins, in part, may well be postulated. But these people, described popularly as "Stone Age" and having, in general, a rather complex agricultural economy, possess all manner of directions of local selection. There are areas of extreme protein deficiency, and there are many areas of iodine deficiency. Under such circumstances it is possible that present genetic diversity may well have developed without any external influences.

5. The Australian Geographical Race today consists of a series of local races clearly allied with the now extinct Tasmanians. As a group, they are big-toothed. In fact, Australian molar sizes often exceed classic European Neanderthals. Like Neanderthals, contemporary Australian aborigines tend to have long and narrow skulls, usually broadest at the base. And they tend to be at least moderately hairy, although perhaps not as hairy as popularly claimed. Some of the rather fine head hair is brown or even red-gold in childhood, the sun-bleached "tawny" hair that Birdsell describes. Male pattern balding and leg (calf) balding are very common among Australian aboriginal men.

Australian aborigines are typically Pacific for the M-N series, having a remarkable excess of N over M. Similarly, the Duffy (Fy^a) gene is very common. But Australian aborigines differ from other Pacific people in the virtual absence of B, Diego-positive, and S in the MN-S series. The sickle-cell gene is similarly absent, there is no G6PD deficiency, and none of the atypical haptoglobins have yet been reported. Together these serological and biochemical peculiarities set them off from Melanesia and Polynesia as well, and together they preclude any recent contact with the African continent or with mainland Asia.

So whatever the Australian aborigines may once have been, their suntanned blackness is not of African make. Their hirsutism, male pattern-balding, and occasional red-gold hair may resemble that of Europeans but not that of any recent Europeans. Except in the Cape York area, there is little evidence of recent contact with New Guinea. In comprising a single polytypic or several polytypic groupings, the Australian aborigines are simply Australian. Ainu-like, Veddoid-like, and Neanderthal-like features may be chance convergence or they may hint at distant origins as yet quite unconfirmed.

6. The Asiatic Geographical Race occupies continental Asia, and extends also to Japan, Taiwan, the Philippines, Indonesia, Sumatra, Borneo, and Java. It encompasses the "little brown

men," the ruggedly tall and often big-eared Tibetans and Mongolians, and the varied peoples of the Asiatic north.

Serologically, Asia is characterized by generally high levels of B, up to 40% in some areas, very high frequencies of the Duffy-positive gene (Fy^a), varying frequencies of Kidd (Jk^a), Diego (Di^a), and β-AIB excretion. Local races and Asiatic micro-races exhibit considerable polymorphism with respect to the major serological factors. Polymorphism for PTC-propylthiouracil taste sensitivity is also considerable, with 40% or more non-tasters in some areas and close to 0% of taste-blind individuals in other areas. Asiatics, like Amerinds, have Gm alleles Gm^a, Gm^{ax}, and Gm^{ab}.

Throughout the Asiatic Geographical Race, "inner" eyefolds are common, body hair is generally spare, male pattern balding is relatively uncommon, and the head hair tends to be coarse (over 100μ in diameter). In much of Asia, limbs are short, relative to the trunk, but this is by no means universal. In the skull, broad malars, shallow orbits, multiple suture bones, and eversion of the gonial region of the jaw are sufficiently common to be individually diagnostic. "Shovelling" of the incisors is common, too, as reviewed by Carbonell.

Polymorphism in the Asiatic Geographical Race is respectably considerable. With a wide range of hot and cold, dry and wet climates, many adaptations to nutritional and caloric deficiencies and intensive direction of disease selection in many areas, it is hardly surprising that the "pure" Mongoloid holotype of the old schoolbooks is rare, if not truly hypothetical. Present problems relate much more to the extent to which protein and caloric deficiency has led to the genetically distinct reduction of skeletal mass in eastern Asiatics. Current problems also include the effects of smallpox selection over the millennia.

7. The Indian Geographical Race extends from the high Himalayas to the Indian Ocean and includes a very large number of local races, "tribes," and micro-races. Being endogamous and of long standing, certain of the Indian castes are valid local races today. Maximum differentiation is seen in the south of India, including groups with markedly Australoid appearance.

To a European, many Indians "look" European, often resembling in facial features the residents of the Middle East and the Arabian peninsula. This facial similarity is hardly surprising, considering the geographical position of India, historical pathways of gene flow, and selective factors in common. The Neolithic in India is clearly related to the Neolithic in the Middle East. But India has long had unique directions of disease selection, and nutritional selection has been particularly intense over the last century, when millions have died in a single famine period.

Serologically, India is characterized by high frequencies of B (up to 35% or more) but low frequencies of r, thus setting it off from continental Europe. M tends to be more frequent than N, a non-European characteristic. Taste-blindness is variable, reaching 43% in the Bombay area. The A_4 genotype for middle phalangeal hair is quite frequent, a non-Mediterranean characteristic by itself. Bone densities appear to be low, despite relatively high intakes of calcium from vegetable sources, again a non-European polymorphism.

It is tempting to view the Indian Geographical Race as drawn from the same populations that originally expanded into Neolithic Europe, the two then becoming divergent by continued selection and reproductive isolation. But this view, probably correct for the most part, is little more than the explanation for human raciation in general. Much more important is the search for particular directions of genetic change, such as smallpox, which may account for the high frequency of blood group B in some areas of India, and the extent to which climatic selection and nutritional selection have made for heavy skin pigmentation and linear build.

8. The European Geographical Race comprises a series of local races and micro-races that has undergone extraordinarily rapid population expansion since 1500, extending its ancient breeding range from North Africa and Western Asia to both Americas, Australia, New Zealand, and much of Africa.

Serologically, the European Geographical Race is unique in the high frequency of the Rh-negative gene (r) and of course A_2 in the ABO series. As a geographical race, including North Africa and the Middle East, it is also unique in the combination of hirsutism, male pattern balding, and delayed tooth eruption. Children of European origin tend to be delayed in the appearance of certain early ossification centers and in some motoric and behavioral skills compared to children elsewhere in the world.

Pigmentation, of course, is notably variable, but the European Geographical Race includes a monopoly of the peoples of minimal melanin development. The north-south axis for pigmentation most strongly suggests climatic or, rather, actinic selection, again pointed out by Blum in his recent symposium. Adaptations to malaria exist in the Mediterranean area and through to Iran. These adaptations include thalassemia, the G6PD deficiency, and familial Mediterranean fever. Cherubism appears to be restricted to the European Geographical Race.

We in the West tend to see more taxonomic complexity in Europe than in other areas, partly because the early taxonomists were Europeans, and partly because we tend to a relatively microscopic and ethnocentric view of man. Still, the European Geographical Race is characterized by considerable local diversity, some of it due to contact beyond its original breeding range, some of it attributable to Pleistocene "remnants," yet much of it unquestionably developed by natural selection *in situ*.

9. The African Geographical Race constitutes a large number of local races and micro-races, all indigenous to Africa, though long carried (as slaves) to Southern Arabia. Besides increased melanin concentration of skin, hair, irises, and gums, the sickle-cell gene (and certain other hemoglobin polymorphisms), the African form of G6PDD, some differences in acclimatized sweat rates, and, in some areas, high frequencies of triquetral-lunate fusions constitute African marker genes. For most polymorphisms, Africa is closer to Europe genetically (as well as geographically).

Serologically, Africa has its own uniquenesses—the frequency of the R_o subtype (up to 70%), the U-negative type in the MNS-U series, the rare gene V, and the Duffy variant Fy. One haptoglobin variant is also distinctive, the so-called Hp^{2m}. So is gamma globulin ab (see Chs. IV and V). Red-green color deficiency is rare in much of Africa, apparently attributable to the late extension of agriculture in many areas, as suggested by Post (1962).

Skin pigmentation is variable in this geographical race; not all of Africa is black. There are areas of less than maximal pigment in East Africa and in South Africa as well. In all areas, however, hair and eye pigment is heavy, and this generally extends to the gums as well. Teeth tend to be accelerated in eruption and third molar teeth are rarely missing in most Africans.

Although helical hair is found elsewhere in the world, the extreme spiral-tuft form of the head hair is characteristically African. So is extreme lip eversion. Steatopygia has a variable distribution but is most common in the extreme south of the African

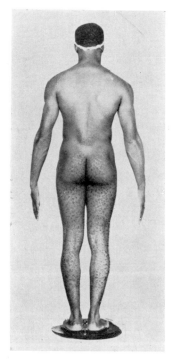

Fig. 26. Spiral-tuft form of the body hair in an American Colored soldier showing the more complete expression of an African gene in a new genotypic combination. "Hybrid" populations also afford tests for linkage and for X- and Y-linkage in particular.

continent, where it appears to be a storage adaptation to the feast-and-famine of hunting-and-gathering life.

As with any numerically large geographical race inhabiting a very wide range of climatic extremes and with different directions of disease selection, African population polymorphism is consid-

Fig. 27. The lighter-skinned, smaller-boned, and smaller-toothed Bushmen of South Africa are characterized by high areolae, *steatopygia*, and early loss of subcutaneous fat. Though sometimes viewed as a separate geographical race, their former geographical range was more extensive than their present limits now suggest.

erable. Attention is now being directed to the distribution of liver cancer in Africa, and into a viral type of lymphoma. When making genetic comparisons of different African groups, we must consider not only the directions of disease selection, but the massive migrations that took place in the last century, following the introduction of new agricultural techniques. We must now consider the advent of European, Indian and Malaysian genes entering in large quantities in some areas of Africa.

SUGGESTED READINGS

Adels, B. R., Francis, J. E., Jr., and Gajdusek, D. C.: Measles in Australasian Indigenes. *Am. J. Dis. Child., 103*:255-260, 1962.

Allison, A. C.: Malaria and glucose-6-phosphate dehydrogenase deficiency. *Nature, 197*:609, 1963.

Blumberg, B. S.: Polymorphisms of the human serum proteins and other biological systems. In Goldschmidt, E. (Ed.) : *The Genetics of Migrant and Isolate Populations*. Baltimore, Williams and Wilkins, 1963.

Blumberg, B. S.: Inherited susceptibility to disease. *Arch. Environm. Health, 3*:612-636, 1961.

*Crenshaw, J. W., Jr.: Direction of human evolution: A zoologist's view. In Garn, S. M. (Ed.) : *Culture and the Direction of Human Evolution*. Detroit, Wayne State University Press, 1964.

Gajdusek, D. C.: Kuru: An appraisal of five years of investigation. *Eugen. Quart., 9*:69-74, 1962.

Garn, S. M.: Reply to Newman, M. T. *Current Anthropol., 4*:197-198, 1963.

Giblett, E. R., and Brooks, L. E.: Haptoglobin sub-types in three racial groups. *Nature, 197*:576-577, 1963.

Haynes, C. V., Jr.: Fluted projectile points: their age and dispersion. *Science, 145*:1408-1413, 1964.

Hulse, F. S.: Race as an evolutionary episode. *Am. Anthropol., 64*: 929-945, 1962.

Kidson, C., and Gorman, J. C.: Contribution of red cell enzyme deficiency trait to an understanding of genetic relationships between Melanesian and other populations, *Am. J. Phys. Anthropol., 20*: 357-363, 1962.

Mayr, E.: The taxonomic evaluation of fossil hominids. In Washburn, S. L. (Ed.) : *Classification and Human Evolution*. Chicago, Aldine Press, 1963.

Newman, M. T.: The application of ecological rules to the racial anthropology of the New World. *Am. Anthropol.,* 55:311-327, 1953.

Post, R. H.: Population differences in vision acuity: A review, with speculative notes on selection relaxation. *Eugen. Quart.,* 9-189-212, 1962.

Singer, R.: The significance of the sickle cell in Africa. *The Leech,* 32:152-161, 1962.

Watson, J. B.: Anthropology in the New Guinea Highlands. *Am. Anthropol.,* 66:4:Part 2, 1964.

XIII

LOCAL RACES

GEOGRAPHICAL RACES are collections of races that occupy a broad geographical area and presumably have common origins. Being relatively few, they can be listed, and we have done so in this book. But geographical races are not prime evolutionary units. As collections of races, they cannot be studied directly. As collections of races, generalizations that can be made about any geographical race need not apply to the component local races.

Local races, in strict contrast, are true evolutionary units. As populations, such local races evolve or have evolved separately. As populations, local microgeographic selective factors tend to be operative in many cases; in other situations, local selection is diluted by gene-interchange. The population, or local population, is the obvious unit for study. In this dynamic unit, the mechanisms of racial change can be ascertained.

Some local races are neatly delimited and simply described. In pre-Columbian America, there were hundreds of such local races, each with its own characteristics, each with its own language. We still recognize the Penobscot, the Pima, the Papago, and so on. Other local races, in the Americas, as in Europe and Asia, constitute a number of isolated or semi-isolated populations as is true for the several Apache and Navajo groups now. With such a diversity of local races, even in one part of the world, it is clearly impossible to make a listing of all of them. We do not have enough information to provide a complete and detailed taxonomy for these smaller groupings of man. And we do not have space to list more than a few.

But it is possible to call attention to some local races that exemplify particular taxonomic, descriptive, or evolutionary problems. There are local races now numbering in the hundreds of millions as a result of historically documented population expansion. There are local races that are small today and represent no real change in numbers over many thousands of years. There are tiny populations, such as the Samaritans, that have remained genetically isolated for millennia and which provide perfect opportunities to study the mechanism of genetic drift, the effects of preferential mating and the effects of inbreeding (Bonné, 1963).

Local races are many, numbering into the thousands. No one can make an exact count; no one would try to. Those local races we give particular attention are so distinguished because of ethnocentricity (the people we know best), or because they are exotic (from our point of view), or because they exemplify known admixture, or because they present problems of taxonomy and questions of origin. They include old named-populations, groupings that deserve more attention, and relatively new populations of historical interest. Some thirty-two are given mention here for these and other reasons, not because there are thirty-two (or 320) or any such number, but simply to give attention to them and to the problems they raise. Not the least of the problems is that of the labels employed, some of them geographical, some linguistic, some less appropriate than others.

Why do we study races? To find out why they exist, why some are huge today and some small, why they diverge in the ways they do, why there are the resemblances that there are. We study races to answer historical questions, to answer phylogenetic questions, to investigate mankind evolving today.

I. Representative Large Local Races

Obvious to all who behold them, and recognized in the literature for years, are some of the large local races of mankind that approach geographical races in size. Representing, for the most part, the more favorable world situations where small local groups underwent rapid population expansion, following the acquisition of new techniques of food production, new sources of energy, or new approaches to public health, these local races are familiar to most of us.

1. **Northwest European.** Originally comprising the hunting peoples of Scandinavia, North Germany, the Low Countries, the

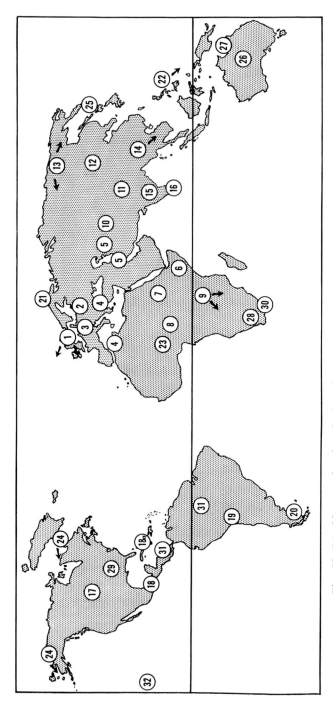

Fig. 28. World map, showing the location of the thirty-two selected local races described in the text.

United Kingdom, and Ireland, it now also includes their descendents abroad. Of primary interest are the selective factors that favored the relative depigmentation that characterizes this local race. Rapid population expansion and migration have together produced many enclaves ideal for study of genetic drift. Some degree of cold adaptation may be presumed for the northernmost members of this local race.

2. **Northeast European.** Currently comprising Poland, Lithuania, Esthonia, and the Great Russias, the major problem currently involves the frequency of blood group B. Though attributed to "Tartar" influences, the frequency of other Asiatic marker traits are not in accord with this explanation. Of equal interest is the historically documented trend towards brachycephalization, which appears to have been considerable in the last 400 years and which may represent directional selection as shown by recent work by T. Bielicki in Poland.

3. **"Alpine."** The traditional name for the rounder-headed and rounder-bodied, somewhat darker people of the Alpine region, through to the Balkans. This is an area in which low iodine intakes may be frequent and therefore the incidence of PTC hypotasters in this region represents a direct test of Boyd's important hypothesis.

4. **Mediterranean.** A long-used label for the darker and generally smaller people of the Mediterranean region from Tangier to the Dardanelles and including the Arabian Peninsula. Multiple adaptations to malaria (in the form of both the abnormal hemoglobins and G6PD deficiency) are found here and such characteristic regionally delimited diseases as hereditary amyloidosis, familial Mediterranean fever, and, apparently, one form of cherubism. Besides their historical origins and subsequent spread over Europe, the Mediterranean Local Race constitutes a series of major problems in geographic medicine.

5. **Iranian.** Primarily the bigger, more rugged, and beakier peoples of Asiatic Turkey through to Iran and India. Current problems involve the G6PD polymorphism in the more malarial areas, and smallpox selection, which may account for the gener-

ally higher frequencies of B in areas where smallpox is now endemic yet associated with relatively low mortality.

6. **East African.** The long-headed, usually quite linear peoples of East Africa to the Sudan, traditionally viewed as an example of simple admixture but equally well viewed as the product of competing directions of selection. It is here that the adaptive value of heavy skin pigmentation can be tested in one of its native habitats.

7. **Sudanese.** Peoples darker than 6, apparently adapted to dry heat (in contrast to the Forest Negro) and lacking the prognathism and more muscular build of the Forest Negro peoples.

8. **Forest Negro.** Deeply pigmented people with very large dental arches, spiral-tuft hair, broad nasal apertures, marked lip eversion, peripheries large as compared to the central mass. The holotype of the "Negro," and comprising the peoples of West Africa and the Congo, with many hemoglobin and haptoglobin variants.

9. **Bantu** (properly a language group). The recently expanding group of peoples whose southward trek collided with European colonization in the last century. One source of African genes is the "Cape Colored" population, and some Gm phenogroups in the Bushmen.

10. **Turkic.** The pastoralists and oasis farmers of central Asia, heavy-set in build and broad of face. The characteristics of this group have been attributed both to admixture and to competing directions of selection. They represent an ideal situation for testing both of these hypotheses.

11. **Tibetan.** The taller, more linear, often Amerind-appearing peoples of Sikkim and Tibet, extending northward to Soviet Mongolia. Possible adaptations to high altitude, severe cold, and low calcium represent problems of current interest.

12. **North Chinese.** The tall and often linear peoples of Northern China, frequently with external eyefolds (in contrast to the above). These are millet and barley eaters. Little modern genetic data currently available.

13. **Extreme Mongoloid.** Siberia, Mongolia to the Kamchatka

Peninsula. The holotype of the hypothetical "Mongoloid." Probably adapted to extreme cold, though confirming information is still lacking. Certainly laboratory and field studies of the metabolic and cardiovascular adaptations to extreme cold should be attempted.

14. **Southeast Asiatic.** An expanding group of generally small-statured peoples, primarily rice eaters, subject to recurrent caloric deprivation, protein deficiency, and hypovitaminosis B_1, C, and, in some cases, A. Besides these limiting nutrients, smallpox, malaria, and leprosy are other active agents of natural selection which may account for the unique serological picture we see today. Note lactase deficiency.

15. **Hindu.** Light brown to very dark-skinned people, now widely spread over the Indian subcontinent. Adaptations to smallpox are probable, especially in the North. Recurrent famine has certainly subjected them to caloric selection. They may be moderately subject to protein selection. Notably, the population has expanded without general improvement in the food supply.

16. **Dravidian.** The heavier peoples of southern India to Ceylon, broad-nosed, darker-skinned, quite "Australoid" in appearance, with some evidence of malarial selection. The major question at hand is their relationship to the Australian aborigines. Some workers hold for a common origin.

II. Amerindian Groups of Local Races

At the time Columbus opened America to the world, the American Indians comprised hundreds of local races, which, in their many migrations, had become fragmented and long separate. Linguistic evidence alone showed that the Navajo and Apache were of Canadian origin and that some of the American Indians of California were similarly displaced far from their original haunts. Characterization of all the American Indian Local Races is impossible, but it is practical to describe at least a few of the major groupings.

17. **North American.** A highly variable, highly polytypic *group* of taller hunting tribes of the United States and Canada.

A_1 is more common than in Central and South America, yet the Diego-positive gene and β-AIB are far less frequent than in Central and South America.

Cerumen polymorphism places the North American "Amerindians" squarely between Asiatic frequencies and European frequencies of the dry-flaky and wet-sticky forms. Gm phenogroups also place American Indians in a relationship to Asiatic peoples.

18. **Central American.** The shorter, often extremely small agricultural people from the American Southwest to Bolivia. Largely O, Hp^1 very common, up to 20 per cent Diego-positive, β-AIB excretion is variable. These people appear to have been adapted to low-protein intake over several millennia. In the Central American highlands, in particular, they are subject to iodine deficiency. The major queston, of course, is the extent to which their present reduced size is genetic as well as environmental in nature. (See both Comas and Layrisse in *Biomedical Challenges Presented by the American Indian,* Pan American Health Organization, Washington D.C., 1968.)

18a. **Caribbean.** These are the coastal, lowland, agricultural, and fishing "Indians" who met Columbus, who first gave us the hammock and tobacco, and who responded to the advent of the Spanish by dying-out in many island areas and in coastal locations in Central America. They are the true "Indians."

19. **South American.** Primarily the agricultural peoples of Peru, Chile, etc. More of them are Diego-positive, β-AIB excretors are more common, and N is somewhat more frequent. These latter features suggest the operation of local selective factors within linguistically related groups. Highly variable in Gm antigens.

20. **Fuegian.** The rugged, non-agricultural inhabitants of southern South America, the Ona, the Yaghan, the Alacaluf, etc. Once viewed as representing the "earliest" inhabitants of the Americas and therefore prototypical of the First Americans, we now view them as representing one extreme of adaptation. Current interest certainly centers on their adaptations to moderate night cold.

III. Puzzling, Isolated, Numerically Small Local Races

There are some human groups that plentifully puzzle the experts. They differ from their neighbors and we ask the reasons why. Some may be representatives of ancient, now-diminished populations. Some may represent bizarre directions of human evolution directed by drift. All are controversial. These numerically small, isolated local races complicate attempts to tailor a tidy taxonomy. That is why they are prime reasons for anthropological study today!

21. **Lapp.** The small-statured, small-toothed, round-headed, almost fragile-appearing fishermen and reindeer herders of the tundra and swamps of West Russia, Finland, and Sweden, regarded as a separate European race by W. C. Boyd and others. Problems include the selective factors responsible for the extremely *high* frequencies of A_2 and certain of the haptoglobin variants, and certainly for their very small teeth which in pattern is different from their neighbors.

22. **Pacific "Negrito."** Small, dark, and frizzly-haired, a series of variable local populations found from Australia to the Philippines. Despite their name, there is no necessary connection with Africa (see Boyd, 1963a, 1963b), but a communality of Pacific origins is at least probable. Research problems concern the antiquity of these populations and the extent to which they have diverged over millennia. Certainly a high-priority group for contemporary investigation.

23. **African Pygmy.** Primarily the Congo pygmies of the Ituri rain forest. One real question is why they are so small. Recent nutritional and biochemical studies show that they are very low in serum cholesterol and they have elevated serum proteins, but there is no immediate answer to their reduced size. In contrast, the comparably small people in Central America, who are truly pygmy of size, clearly suffer from protein-deficiency diseases.

With recent work on Gm phenogroups pygmy uniqueness stands out whereas conventional blood groups failed to emphasize differences.

24. **Eskimo.** Two, three, or possibly more geographically restricted populations, broken into numerous small breeding groups and evidencing a variety of metabolic and vascular adaptations to the extreme cold. Radiocarbon dates now suggest considerable antiquity in Alaska, 3,000 years or more. The major problem, of course, is whether the Eskimos really have a single origin or whether they comprise multiple movements of Siberian and Amerindian groups that, having attained a particular technological level, moved into the Arctic.

IV. Long-Isolated Marginal Local Races

Certain populations in odd corners of the habitable world have been isolated for thousands of years. These populations include some of the most remote and most exotic human groups. Historically, many of them are among the most "ancient" isolated human populations and, in some cases, may even be examples of our Pleistocene ancestors frozen in chronological time. Certainly, they have been touched least by modern selective factors.

In one sense, such ancient population samples represent a modern glimpse into human racial antiquity. In another sense, they provide examples of human beings crowded into ecologically narrow niches. In all cases, they are prime situations to test for genetic drift.

25. **Ainu.** The legendary hairy Ainu of Northern Japan, bear-worshipping and the apparent remnant of a much larger pre-Neolithic group that inhabited areas of mainland China and Taiwan as well. Not as hairy as earlier claimed, the Ainu do have the Gm alleotype $Gm,^{2,17,21}$ which is apparently uniquely Ainu as well as three Gm phenogroups shared with Asiatics in general. The simplest taxonomic position of the Ainu is simply Ainu.

26. **Murrayian** and 27. **Carpenterian Australian.** Two groups of hunting populations, at least one showing multiple adaptations to moderate night cold. Their small local groups or "hordes," the size of which is neatly tied to available rainfall, are ideal laboratories for the study of genetic drift. Extreme values of blood group N (up to 1.00) suggest that M may be especially disadvantageous in Australasia. So far, we do not even have a single notion why.

28. **Bushmen** and **Hottentots.** The aboriginal inhabitants of South Africa, certainly less melanotic than most other members of the African Geographical Race, and showing specialized areas of fat storage (that is, steatopygia). They have extreme peppercorn hair and early loss of subcutaneous fat. With very small groups, approaching the theoretical minimum population size in man, the "Bushmen" of South Africa afford a contrasting natural laboratory for the study of genetic drift. Again, as some have now come to be migrant farm workers, we are able to investigate the effect of the altered dietary habits on their size and growth.

V. "Hybrid" Local Races of Recent Origin

Although all recent and most extinct species of man are "hybrid" in the sense that they have acquired genes from others, this term is generally restricted to situations involving two or more geographical races. Many such combinations are known, and they offer the advantage of historical data, and they present new genotypic combinations for us to consider. But, as we try to calculate the original proportions of admixture from different genetically determined traits, we discover that the separate estimates, while reasonably similar, are not identical. Clearly, selection has taken place in such hybrid groups. Hybrid races, therefore, are moving toward new adaptive modes. By investigating them, we can catch ongoing human evolution on the march!

29. **North American Colored ("American Negro").** The so-called Colored or Negro populations of the United States, Bermuda, the West Indies, and Canada. Of West-Africa and Northwest-European origin, the accretion of European genes due to continuing admixture is partially balanced by the social phenomenon of "crossing over." Besides providing possibilities for testing genetic linkage, such recent and hybrid populations as the American Colored provide an opportunity for testing differential selection at different gene loci is Pollitzer has done. See also the work of Reed, and note the current preference for the label *Black*.

30. **South African Colored ("Cape Colored").** The analogous population of South Africa, including Bushmen-Hottentot and Bantu genes with a variable contribution of European, Malaysian,

and Indian genes. Here, nutritional selection, tuberculosis selection, and, in some areas, malarial selection provide potential problems for study.

31. **Ladino.** Southern European and southern Amerindian, but including also (in the breeding population) unmixed Amerindians who have adopted the "Ladino" way of life. As with the preceding recently formed populations, there is great local polymorphism due to diversity of actual origins. Depending on local attitudes, Ladino groups in Central and South America may acknowledge little or no Amerindian in their origins, or little or no European in their ancestry. The persistence of the Diego-positive gene in the mixed Ladino populations in South America may provide some understanding of the meaning of this serological polymorphism.

32. **Neo-Hawaiian.** A highly variable complex of northwest European and southern European with Polynesian and Chinese/Japanese and Filipino admixture. This population, still changing, has hardly reached panmixia and in many respects the Hardy-Weinberg law does not quite pertain. But it is now the outstanding laboratory situation for the comparative study of human racial "hybrids" under optimum living conditions and where prejudice is still at a minimum. This hybrid population further provides the best modern test for heterosis; that is outbreeding, in modern man.

SUGGESTED READINGS

Allison, A. C., Askonas, B. A., Barnicot, N. A., Blumberg, B. S., and Krimbas, C.: Deficiency of erythrocyte glucose-6-phosphate dehydrogenase in Greek populations. *Annals Human Genet., 26:*237-242, 1963.

Barnicot, N. A., Allison, A. C., Blumberg, B. S., Deliyannis, G., Krimbas, C., and Ballas, A.: Haemoglobin types in Greek populations. *Annals Human Genet., 26:*229-236, 1963.

Blackwell, R. Q., and Huang, J. T.: Abnormal hemoglobin studies in Taiwan aborigines. *Science, 139:*771-772, 1963.

Bonné, B.: The Samaritans: a demographic study. *Human Biol., 35:* 61-89, 1963.

Goldschmidt, E., Bayani-Sioson, P., Sutton, H. E., Friend, K., Sandor,

A., and Bloch, N.: Haptoglobin frequencies in Jewish communities. *Annals Human Genet., 26:*39-46, 1962.

Gorman, J. G., and Kidson, C.: Distribution pattern of an inherited trait, red cell enzyme deficiency, in New Guinea and New Britain. *Am. J. Phys. Anthropol., 20:*347-356, 1962.

Hereditary Amyloidosis?, *J.A.M.A.,* May 4, 1963, p. 418.

Hulse, F.: Warfare, demography and genetics. *Eugen. Quart., 8:*185-197, 1961.

Johnson, C. W.: Steatopygia of the human female in the Kalahari. *Professional Geographer, 14:*1-3, 1962.

Kalmus, H., Amir, A., Levine, O., Barak, E., and Goldschmidt, E.: The frequency of inherited defects of colour vision in some Israeli populations. *Annals Human Genet., 25:*51-55, 1961.

Matsunaga, E., and Murai, K.: Genetic study of haptoglobin types in a Japanese population. *Proc. 8th Congress Int. Soc. Blood Transf.,* Tokyo, 1962, pp. 397-400.

Neumann, M. A., Gajdusek, D. C., and Zigas, V.: Neuro-pathologic findings in exotic neurologic disorders among natives of the highlands of New Guinea. *J. Neuropath. Exp. Neurol., 23:*486-507, 1964.

Pollitzer, W. S.: Analysis of a tri-racial isolate. *Human Biol., 36:*362-373, 1964.

Sheba, C., Ashkenazi, I., and Szeinberg, A.: Taste senstitivity to phenylthiourea among the Jewish population groups in Israel. *Am. J. Human Genet., 14:*44-51, 1962.

XIV

LIVING RACES AND FOSSIL TAXA

T HE STUDY of living human races has every advantage,
or nearly. The number of subjects is usefully large, even in the
tiniest Amazon isolate. The number of polymorphisms that can
be investigated is large, and daily growing larger. In most cases
past technical errors can now be corrected, and past assumptions
as to taxonomic position and phylogenetic relationships can be
newly revised. In the ten years since *Human Races* first appeared,
much new information has been added, many taxonomic judgements have been reconsidered, some of them minor and some
major. Our understanding of directed and nondirected genetic
change in living man has greatly improved; advances are truly
far more than terminological and improvements far more than
just data-accumulation.

When we turn to fossil forms of man, those of our own species,
those of earlier *erectus* hominids, and those of still-earlier species
still in taxonomic uncertainty, most of these advantages can no
longer be counted. Not one single-generation true fossil "population" is known. No single group of fossils from a single site equals
in number a single living Bushman band. The fossils cannot tell
us their group identification (as living men can easily do) nor
their generational relationships, nor their habits. We cannot infer
the extent of size reduction because of malnutrition and infection,
as with still-living groups, nor even sex, with decent certainty.
Given ten fossils from some assembled group, we merely hope
that half were males and half were females, within $\pm$ 30%.

To add to all fossil problems, we are forced to make taxonomic
judgements under extremely difficult circumstances, usually within a species, not horizontally (at a given time) but vertically
(covering both time and space). We have but one advantage, and
that comes from the living model, through the use of living races
as models for fossil taxa. *Homo* is not dead, but alive and expand-

ing his numbers. We employ our knowledges of men of the present to clarify our thinking about men of the past. No fossil judgement can possibly be made in isolation from our knowledge of the living, though in earlier days of fossil hunting and fossil naming, the knowledge was not always there nor was it always used.

The body-size range of living human populations is limited, not quite 10% at most, and that includes major nutritional extremes. This is well within the 15% size range of a species and indicates the size plateau to which *sapiens* is adapted, and, apparently, *erectus* too. From this very point of view, much smaller population means for some fossil would indicate a separate species and a different adaptive plateau, which may or may not bear on the taxonomic position of the "Australopithecines."

Sexual size dimorphism in living hominids is both small (for primates) and large (for primates). It is the order of 7%, males 175 cm and females 165 cm, for example. Relative size dimorphism is pretty much the same from Lapps to Watusi, from the truly tiny Mayan-speaking Indians of Guatemala to the size elite in Texas and Oklahoma. It is not probable that human size dimorphism was vastly different in *erectus* and not very probable that we now are the final progeny of a form of *Homo* greatly different in size dimorphism either. The same may be said of the teeth, wherein crown-size dimorphism in modern man is of the order of 3% to 5%, truly small by baboon standards, but possibly indicating that in tooth size as in body size, our own line was never notable in having truly big-toothed males and small-toothed females. Even the largest-toothed of living groups, such as the Pima Indians, are modest in tooth-size dimorphism among the primates that we know, except for *Hylobates*.

Much the same can be said of the canine teeth. In man today, taking several dozen measured groups into consideration, canine dimorphism is rather modest, compared, say, to *Papio*. It becomes less likely that there was some sudden evolutionary break, some dramatic divergence from big-canined ancestral males, and a greater likelihood that our line was long characterized by relatively little canine dimorphism. As with body size (that is, stature) we are probably not the sports of an ancestral form with

SOME APPLICATIONS OF PRESENT POPULATIONS TO THE
FOSSIL PAST

Author	Polymorphism	Findings
Garn and Koski (1957) Koski and Garn (1957) Garn and Lewis (1969)	"Fossil" eruption sequence	The M2P2 or "fossil" eruption sequence claimed as unique for older "palaeanthropic" fossils proved to be an artifact due to comparison of alveolar eruption in fossils with gingival eruption in the living. For all groups, M2 tends to precede P2 in calcification and crown enlargement.
Garn and Lewis (1958) Garn, Lewis, and Kerewsky (1968)	Tooth-size body-size relationships	Within individuals, tooth-size, body-size correlations are low (circa 0.2) but positive indicating some communality but little predictability. Between populations and between species, no regular relationship can be demonstrated.
Garn, Lewis, and Kerewsky (1963)	Molar size sequences	The M2>M1 size sequence, previously considered as "fossil" is found in 10% to 20% of modern subjects.
Garn (1966) Garn, Lewis, and Kerewsky (1966) Garn, Lewis, Swindler, and Kerewsky (1967)	Sexual dimorphism in tooth size	Crown size sexual dimorphism in *Homo sapiens* is of the order of 2% to 4%, small compared to many primates, but larger than in *Hylobates agilis*.
Garn (1963)	Cranial thickness	Cranial thickness values in modern man may exceed that in fossils believed to be uniquely thick-skulled.
Garn (1963)	Tooth size	The range of molar sizes in subjects of European origin encompasses or even exceeds values for Skuhl, Krapina and even "Sinanthropus" and "Pithecanthropus."
Garn (1966)	Canine field	The greater sexual dimorphism in canine size actually exists as a field including also I^2 and P^1. Overall, there are multiple "fields" in the dentition and present and past hominids reflect many distinct divergences in such fields.

big-canined bulking males using dental threat and canine display to maintain and preserve their harem, but rather the continuation of a line of limited canine dimorphism, through evolutionary time.

Having modern man to study in abundance, from Andamanese

to Zulus, it is simple to reject the notion that early man, or earlier man, had unusually thick skulls. We have far too much information now, including the evidence for continuing accretion of skull thickness with advancing age. Taking the measure of modern man it is possible to employ tooth size in Australian aborigines and New Guinea natives and Pima Indians from the American Southwest to show that the various Neandertals or Neanderthals were not so large of dental crown, and in some cases rather small. The more we learn of the living the more we can say of the past.

In recent issues of *Current Anthropology* (*10*:179, *11*:79) there has been considerable discussion of the possible adaptive value of *erectus* skull thickness without consideration of actual thicknesses of skulls, either fossil or modern and without considering the possibility that the species label *erectus* has been assigned to many specimens simply on the basis of skull thickness! Since many modern people of European ancestry exceed the classic Javanese-Chinese *erectus* forms in skull thickness, in part a manifestation of hyperostosis cranii, it is more than likely that the species *erectus* now includes specimens of several species who simply had the fortune to have thick skulls or maybe Paget's disease.

We can reject the M2P2 "fossil" sequence of tooth eruption as uniquely fossil and the M2>M1 size sequence as having taxonomic significance. We can show now that tooth size has not been systematically or regularly diminished over a quarter of a million years, and we can show (from the study of modern men) that neither the anterior teeth nor the posterior teeth have been disproportionately diminished as part of a regular evolutionary trend. We can use the crown-size profile pattern as a taxonomic aid in living populations, but the very same approach then makes the provisional genera "Australopithecus" and "Paranthropus" rather less divergent, indeed no more different *patternwise* than two related groups of living men today.

Using living man as an inevitable guide, the higher and lower taxonomic groupings for comparison, the fossils seem less different, less distinct, less "fossil" now. It becomes easier to see more of them as co-specific with us at least, and co-generic at most, than

in the days when each fossil skull or fragment was accorded a
genus and a species uniquely all of its own. We need not now
postulate major breaks in hominid evolution to account for differences that are not so very different or to explain trends that were
not necessarily trends at all. We need not fashion elaborate hypotheses to explain evolutionary trends that never were.

At the same time we have learned enough not to equate any
single group, fossil or living, with any other. No two groups are
taxonomically quite equivalent. The situations are inevitably
unalike. The Eskimos dot the tops of two worlds, but each Eskimo
group now exchanges more genes with non-Eskimo neighbors.
We observe the Eskimos and their language, the Bushmen and
their speech, but while observing both, neither are close taxonomic equivalents. From such examples, now or formerly covering vast territories, we have greater difficulties still in respect to
the proverbial Neandertals. Covering three continents, in one
estimate a quarter-million years of time, were all Neandertals or
Neanderthals genuinely "Neanderthal"? Or are they a collection
of types at best?

With living man now we can avoid typology, the art or non-
science of pulling out look-alikes regardless of group. True, there
is a native of Queensland who resembles Ben Gurion, and an
Aleut from Umnak who resembles a noted Hollywood director.
Yet, we have learned not to play typology when we have living
populations. This is less easy to remember when our "population"
is purely skeletal, Mound-builder or Hopewellian, and least easy,
in turn, with truly fossil remains. With a fossil here and a fossil
there and a fragment in a third place much removed, all that remains from ten million miles of space times a hundred thousand
years of time, there is little else we can do but typology. If a fossil
in South Africa more or less resembles one from Java, it is in-
escapable that we bet on similarities and infer relationships based
on type.

In this typological situation that the sheer paucity of fossil
remains forces upon us, we do have living man as a working
model, or better a series of working models. We can, by radio-

graphs, accumulate much comparative material on the living. We can make judgements as to probable size from bone-size–stature relationships. We can make some estimate of sex, within broad limits, and we are in a better position to say how much those fossils diverge, not just from the old ethnocentric comparison with too-few German and not-ten French skeletons, but by comparison with more appropriate and more extensive models now.

The study of living groups has appeal of its own, not the least being the measurement of evolutionary change today. It has appeal in establishing taxonomic relationships in the living, and establishing, or hoping to establish, broad phylogenetic affinities as well. It has appeal, moreover, in relation to men of the past, of our species, and of species preceding. One of the uses of the present is to clarify the past, and so we employ living races to understand and establish fossil taxa. To be sure, no group now is identical in breeding structure and selective pressures with any past population, no more than to any other group now living. But when it comes to body size and sexual dimorphism, to variability, to canine dimensions and cranial vault thickness, to tooth eruption sequence, or metacarpal-phalangeal relationships, or vertebral height it is inevitable that living man is the reference or the model for fossil taxa.

Those who study the living do so because of living problems, many quite removed from fossil concerns. PKU and maple-sugar urine, middle-phalangeal hair, simian creases, brachymesophalangia, and amyloid disease are far removed from the classic dimensions of bone and teeth. The results and the knowledge may then apply to the long dead as well as to the quick and the living, to recent microevolutionary history and to long-term macro-evolutionary trends. Living races relate to fossil taxa, surely within the confines of our species and, lacking other models, to hominids of different kinds. As we clarify our knowledge of modern man, living in greatest numerical abundance, we simplify our understanding of now-extinct forms, for whom we serve without any alternative as reference models, so employing the living for the elucidation of the past.

SUMMARY

Living races of *Homo* usefully serve as models for fossil taxa. Fossil variability must be compared with population variability now, inferences as to fossil sex are based on sexual dimorphisms in living men, and claims as to fossil uniqueness may be balanced against knowledge of population polymorphisms and population ranges in still-living groups of men. Despite limits to the use of the living as exact models for the now-extinct, knowledge of living races has greatly clarified our comprehension of fossils, of our species, of other species, and for those designated by separate labels as provisional genera.

SUGGESTED READINGS

Garn, S. M.: Culture and the direction of human evolution. *Hum. Biol., 35:*221-236, 1963.

Garn, S. M.: A canine "field" in the sexual dimorphism in tooth size. *Nature, 24:*1501-1502, 1966.

Garn, S. M.: Taxonomy in recent and fossil man. In Garn, S. M. (Ed.) : *Readings on Race,* Springfield, C C Thomas 1968.

Garn, S. M., Dahlberg, A. A., Lewis, A. B., and Kerewsky, R. S.: Genetic independence of Carabelli's trait from tooth size or crown morphology. *Arch. Oral Biol., 11:*745-747, 1966.

Garn, S. M., and Koski, K.: Tooth eruption sequence in fossil and recent man. *Nature, 180:*442-443, 1957.

Garn, S. M., and Lewis, A. B.: Tooth-size, body-size and "giant" fossil man. *Am. Anthropol., 60:*874-880, 1958.

Garn, S. M., and Lewis, A. B.: Phylogenetic and intra-specific variations in tooth sequence polymorphism. In Brothwell, D. R. (Ed.) : *Dental Anthropolgy,* London, Pergamon 1963.

Garn, S. M., Lewis, A. B., and Kerewsky, R. S.: Molar size sequences and fossil taxonomy. *Science, 142:*1060, 1963.

Garn, S. M., Lewis, A. B., and Kerewsky, R. S.: Sex difference in tooth shape. *J. Dent. Res., 46:*1470, 1967.

Garn, S. M., Lewis, A. B., and Kerewsky, R. S.: The magnitude and implications of the relationship between tooth size and body size. *Arch. Oral Biol., 13:*129-131, 1968.

Garn, S. M., Lewis, A. B., Swindler, D. R., and Kerewsky, R. S.: Genetic control of sexual dimorphism in tooth size. *J. Dent. Res., 46:* 963-972, 1967.

Garn, S. M., Lewis, A. B., and Walenga, A. J.: Crown-size profile pattern comparisons of 14 human populations. *Arch. Oral Biol., 13:* 1235-1242, 1968.

Koski, K., and Garn, S. M.: Tooth eruption sequence in fossil and modern man. *Am. J. Phys. Anthropol., N.S. 15:*469-488, 1957.

XV

THE STUDY OF RACE

There are at least fourteen good reasons to study race in living man. These are as follows:

1. To establish affinities, as when comparing various groups of pygmies in Africa.

2. To determine why size and other extremes exist, as in the various African pygmies.

3. To ascertain broad phylogenetic relationships, as when seeking Asiatic origins for β-AIB, brachymesphalangia, and Diego in the American Indians, or dry-wet cerumen.

4. To relate polymorphisms both to common origins and to selective mechanisms, as with hemoglobin S and the various G6PD red-cell deficiencies.

5. To test for the founder effect and the grandfather effect, to measure drift and other non-directed sources of genetic change and genetic difference.

6. To compare different measure of genetic difference, by serology, by morphology, by serum proteins and haptoglobins and transferrins.

7. To measure the rate of ongoing evolution in contemporary man, at loci now known and others becoming discovered.

8. To measure the effects of admixture, the loss of genes, the piling up of genes, to recreate the ancestral genetic proportions, and again to test mathematical measures of distance.

9. To illuminate the understanding of past populations in the light of present groups; to clarify the taxonomy of extinct forms of *Homo* using data from men now living.

10. To comprehend the meaning of genetically determined disease and to relate such disorders to infectious diseases, to breeding structure, to phylogeny, and to microevolutionary changes.

11. To provide a public health picture of congenital disorders, neonatal and adult disorders of genetic origin, and to clarify the genetic load of each population for its own benefit and good.

12. To find adaptations to climate, altitude, and nutrition (or to disprove them) ; to separate genetic race from the accidents of geography or the products of malnutrition and infection.

13. To ascertain racial differences in the rate, timing, and sequence of growth events, and at the same time to separate biological race from the biology of nutrition and infection and parasitization that affect the rate and duration of growth.

14. To measure the extent of chromosomal differentiation, in our species, not just for the Y chromosome, but for the autosomes, including translocations and minor short-arm and long-arm differences, in the frequency of chromosomal losses and in losses related to age.

LABELS FOR HUMAN RACES

As WITH HOMINID TAXONOMY at every level, human groupings below the species present inevitable problems of labels. What we call a group is a complex product of history, tradition, and emotional appeal.

The native peoples of the Americas got to be called *Indians* because Columbus made a 13,000 mile mistake. The people of Europe are still often called *Caucasians* because Blumenbach (1795) thought Caucasian women fairest of them all.

The term *Nordic,* for Northern, is an "out" term because it was turned into a hypothetical race riding out of Asia, and later a basis for Nazi racism. The label *Bantu* bears some objections because it is a language term, but so also is Eskimo and Turkish.

The NAACP earlier specified *American Colored* as the acceptable term for use in earlier editions of *Human Races* as against Negro or Black. Today, younger members of the NAACP prefer "Black," and insist on its use. In Australia, the Blacks are another geographical race away.

Prior to 1946, the term *Arab* was restricted to Arabic-speaking peoples from Arabia. Since that time it has been extended to include non-Arabian, non Arabic-speaking and non-Moslem groups. Since 1960 people of Mexico origin in the U.S.A. have increasingly been called *Chicanos,* a tag now being extended to other Spanish-speaking groups at the same time that the designation "Anglo" has been locally extended to include all of European origin!

With changing political boundaries, Bohemians (of the earlier literature) are hard to locate, and Upper Voltans and Gambians are difficult to place in the older data. Navahos are now properly spelled *Navajos,* by specification of the tribal (now national) council.

On the one hand, it seems appropriate to call people what they prefer, and to employ their orthography. On the other hand there is need to preserve continuity in naming. On the third hand, in citing data and summarizing studies, the labels employed by scientists need to be retained, though noting that one man's *Caucasians* include East Indians, another survey's Caucasians includes Puerto Ricans, and that in some early census data, people originating in Africa, Asia, and natives of North and Central America were pooled together!

As with hominid taxonomy in general, classification of living human races raises problems of labels. For the fossils, one must observe the rule of priority, yet avoid premature elevation of provisional names to true generic or species rank and avoid fossilization of no-longer-valid labels simply because they were once used. For the living, dealing with groups below the species level, the problem of labels is complicated by the politics and the preferences of groups designated. This, applied to the spelling "Navajo," to "Aleuts" rather than "Aleut," and to "Negro," at this writing, is said to be acceptable if the initial letter is not capitalized.

INDEX